I'LL HOLD YOU
WHILE IT HURTS

To order additional copies of *I'll Hold You While It Hurts,*
by Arthur Milward, **call 1-800-765-6955.**

Visit us at **www.reviewandherald.com** for information
on other Review and Herald® products.

True Stories That Take You Straight to the Arms of God

I'LL HOLD YOU WHILE IT HURTS

Arthur A. Milward

REVIEW AND HERALD® PUBLISHING ASSOCIATION
HAGERSTOWN, MD 21741-1119

The Review and Herald® Publishing Association publishes biblically-based materials for spiritual, physical, and mental growth and Christian discipleship.

This book was
Edited by Lori Peckham
Cover design by Tina Ivany
Interior design by Candy Harvey
Cover photo by PictureQuest
Electronic makeup by Shirley M. Bolivar
Typeset: 11/14 Bembo

PRINTED IN U.S.A.

10 09 08 07 06 5 4 3 2 1

R&H Cataloging Service
Milward, Arthur A.
I'll hold you while it hurts: the best true stories of Arthur A. Milward.

1. Short stories.
I. Title.

8-8.888

ISBN 978-0-8280-1887-6x

For my beloved sons and daughters,
for my precious grandchildren,
and
for all the students of all ages
who have shared their lives with me.
Thank you.

CONTENTS

INTRODUCTION

"I will not leave you comfortless: I will come to you" (John 14:18).

This is one of my two most precious Bible promises—neither of which, over many years, has ever failed me.

Not only does the Lord, who yearns over us and, amazingly, longs for our companionship, promise to comfort us, but He promises us His very presence.

He was there with the three young men in the fiery furnace, sharing in their experience. He not only died for our salvation, but, in the person of His Son, He came to live with us—again, to fully share in our experience as a human being.

He even, during the final moments of His incarnation, shared His crucifixion experience with two other humans—two felons, no less.

He could have done nothing more to emphasize His complete identification with us as human beings.

The other promise, also from my caring, compassionate heavenly Father but "filtered" through the agency of one of His children, was vitally important to me as a young child. Having very limited contact with my parents, I ("Boo," according to my sister) was signally blessed to be in the care of a Christian, notably compassionate and understanding, nanny—a woman who had spent her entire adult life loving and caring for other people's children.

Recognizing my tendency to "fall apart" under stress, Nanny, on countless occasions when I was hurting, physically or emotionally, put her arms around me and assured me, gently and uncritically: "I can't stop it hurting right now, Boo, but I'll hold you while it hurts."

I'LL HOLD YOU WHILE IT HURTS

I am essentially unable to distinguish between the arms of my heavenly Father and the arms of my beloved Nanny, who, by her caring concern, demonstrated and reflected His love for me so often and so compassionately. Though she is gone now these many years, I love her still.

Why did our Creator-Father feel the need to create another race of beings? He created us because He needed someone else to love, and to love Him back. The realization that I am one of those created for this purpose is, indeed, "too wonderful for me . . . I cannot attain unto it" (Psalm 139:6).

CREDO

I came to a realization of the existence of my Creator, my heavenly Father, quite early in life, albeit initially very dimly and tentatively, and in a somewhat unorthodox fashion.

Growing up in a quite remote area of North Derbyshire in England, on the edge of the moors, and having very limited contact with my parents (although living in the same house), I was essentially a solitary child.

My initial stirrings of wonderment concerning the—to me—incredibly beautiful world into which I had been born, and questionings as to its purpose, came to me, I recognized a good deal later, through the "whisperings" of the Holy Spirit as I lay motionless in the heather on the moors adjacent to my home, waiting for the beautiful, wonderful denizens of the area to approach me.

I was fascinated by anything that ran, hopped, crawled, slithered, flew, or even swam. They were a never-ending wonder to me, and I longed—even yearned—for a closer contact with them.

I spent countless hours lying quite motionless in the grass and heather, waiting for one or another of these fascinating creatures to approach me and permit me the joy of a closer acquaintance.

Occasionally accompanied by my sister, Mary, only a year and a half my senior, I discovered that if I lay perfectly still, made no sudden movements, and remained very quiet, one or another of the "local inhabitants," overcome by curiosity, would lose its fear of me and approach me, even employing some part of my person as a resting place or as a vantage point from which to survey the landscape.

This was ecstasy for me. I convinced myself that the mouse, the bunny, or even the lizard loved me, trusted me, and knew I meant it no harm.

"Where did all this beauty come from?" I asked myself. Something, someone, must have designed it. Why?

Having had no formal religious instruction and virtually no exposure to the Bible, my initial "instruction" in these matters was, by God's grace, provided directly by the ministry of the Master Teacher, the Holy Spirit Himself.

Later, with access to the "love letter" addressed to me that He had dictated, I learned more. I learned who it was who had brought about all the beauty and wonder that surrounded me. I learned that He had conceived and created it for me—because He loved me.

In the quite isolated, self-contained environment in which I grew up, there were few "significant others" in my world—four, to be precise: my beloved Nanny; my little "big sister," Mary; Aunt Bertha, Nanny's unmarried sister; and Peggy, my cat.

I knew, without a shadow of a doubt, that Nanny loved me unconditionally, without reservation. I relied heavily on Mary, who, always caring and resourceful, so often "put me back together" when I "fell apart." I was equally convinced that Aunt Bertha, for no reason at all, loved me and found me wonderful. Peggy, my confidant and frequent companion, was one of the "angels with furry faces" that have also reflected His love for me.

My precious family, my beloved friends, and so many "casual" acquaintances, most especially the many beautiful children whom I have encountered as we crossed paths through the years, have reflected His love for me in a smile, a look, a brief exchange.

I am firmly convinced that our "gospel commission" is by no means confined to efforts of indoctrination and proselytization. I truly believe that we are—that I am—called rather to respond to the heartfelt cry of so many, often silently, even unwittingly, echoing the urgent appeal voiced by Philip: "Lord, show us the Father" (John 14:8).

Our commission, our raison d'être, our purpose for living, I believe, is just that: by the grace of God, and through the agency of His sweet Spirit, to, however dimly, reflect the character of our Lord—His love and compassion—to those we are privileged to contact.

I am assured that if only one of God's children responds positively to the invitation of His Spirit because that one has seen a glimpse of His caring love in us, there will be joy in heaven, and the angels will sing (see Luke 15). This I believe.

WRITE HER A POEM
(EVERYBODY SENDS FLOWERS)

When I was 7 years old, I wrote a poem. There was this girl, you see . . . I was living in England, close to a remote North Derbyshire village, and I was, for the most part, in the care of a nanny, as was every properly brought-up young person of the social stratum to which I belonged.

One of the most eagerly anticipated events in my well-ordered life was the weekly visit with my nanny to her home in the village. We would spend the afternoon with her sister, "Aunt Bertha," discussing current events and social problems.

When we had national and local affairs settled to our satisfaction, I would, if the day was a fine one, be permitted to go outside the cottage and wander around in the extensive kitchen garden and the adjoining apple orchard behind the house.

That was how I met Edith. She lived next door, and her home was separated from the garden of Laburnum Cottage by a low picket fence.

I had observed her from a distance on a number of occasions, but it wasn't until I had an opportunity for a closer confrontation that her true fascination struck me.

She came over to the fence one afternoon and stood watching me. I was engrossed in one of my favorite pastimes—racing caterpillars. This—in case you are unacquainted with it—is a satisfying but often frustrating sport. It is particularly difficult to keep the contestants all headed in the same direction, a problem that renders the activity more challenging to the race promoter.

After watching my activities silently over the fence, the small neighbor evidently had a brainstorm. She disappeared—somewhat to my disappointment, for although we had neither spoken a word to each other nor acknowledged each other's existence in any way, I couldn't help feeling that for an activity of the sort in which I was engaged, an audience—even a silent audience—was something of an asset.

To my surprise and, I think, my pleasure, she returned almost immediately with a cat in her arms. "This one of yours?" she inquired. "I mean, Miss Fern's?"

Aunt Bertha always had lots of cats, so I wasn't closely acquainted with them all and wasn't prepared to vouch for the identity of the one proffered to me across the fence. Still, I examined the animal closely, seeking any identifying mark I remembered, but found none. The cat, in turn, eyed me a trifle suspiciously from the sheltering arms.

"I really don't know," I admitted, "but I'll find out. Wait a minute."

Taking the cat from her arms, I carried the animal into the house and exhibited him to Aunt Bertha, who recognized him immediately. I set him down and went back outside. The girl still stood on her side of the fence, awaiting my return. She looked at me inquiringly.

"Yes," I assured her. "He's one of ours." And, after a pause, "Thank you."

She blushed faintly, tugged at the hem of her dress in a sort of token curtsy, turned, and ran back down the path and into her house.

I abandoned my caterpillars and dashed into the cottage to tell Aunt Bertha about my newfound friend.

"Aunt Bertha," I said, the words tumbling over each other in my excitement, "did you know that there's a little girl next door who is just about as old as me?"

"Oh, yes," replied Aunt Bertha with amazing calmness. "That's Edith Scattergood. Her daddy makes coffins."

A little bewildered by this matter-of-fact acceptance of such a notable event, I pressed for further information.

The information I elicited was scanty. I had already been told her name, and she was indeed about the same age as I—6 or 7 years old.

"She's a sweet lass," summed up Aunt Bertha.

The next time I paid a visit to Laburnum Cottage it was raining, so I had to stay in the house all afternoon and was unable to pursue my acquaintance with the fascinating girl next door.

The following week, however, was warm and sunny, and as soon as I arrived at the cottage I requested and received permission to play outside.

Edith was standing on the other side of the fence in just about the same spot I had seen her two weeks before. This time, however, she held no cat in her arms.

"Good afternoon, Edith," I greeted her, somewhat formally. "I am going to race some caterpillars when I have caught some."

She smiled shyly at me. "I'll catch some for you," she offered. "There's lots on our gooseberry and black currant bushes."

She ran off down the garden path and disappeared into the tangle of fruit bushes that constituted about half of her family's kitchen garden. In a few minutes she returned to the fence. Her blond hair was in disarray, she had mud on her knees, and there were scratches on her bare, brown arms. Her eyes were shining as she held out her cupped hands to me across the fence.

She had not exaggerated her ability to furnish contestants for my projected race. In her hands she had 17 wriggling caterpillars. There were some long, thin, green ones; some short, fat, black ones; and a number of the spotted, furry ones that I found the most satisfying to handle.

"Thank you very much, Edith," I said enthusiastically. "You really are a super caterpillar catcher"—and sensing that perhaps something more was called for—"and you're really pretty, too."

Edith blushed and lowered her eyes. Looking at her across our squirming handfuls, I realized that my attempt at gallantry was not unjustified.

She transferred the wrigglers from her hands to mine, and we fell to discussing the relative merits of the different types of caterpillars. We agreed that the long, greenish ones were undoubtedly the best racers, but that the short, furry ones made the most satisfying pets.

"Why don't you come over the fence and help me race them?" I invited. "It would be much more fun if you would."

She blushed again. "Oh, no, I couldn't do that," she declared, scandalized. "It wouldn't be proper. Anyway, I've got to go in now and help get my dad's tea."

"But you're all scratched," I objected, trying to delay her departure for a few more moments. "And your hair's all tangled from the gooseberry bushes. Let me smooth it down for you."

Depositing my caterpillars in a safe place between two big rocks, I ran my fingers through her shining hair, smoothing the tangles and picking out the leaves she had collected in her passage through the bushes.

Finally I had it all smoothed out, but I continued to stroke her hair. I enjoyed the golden, silky feel of it under my fingers. Edith seemed to like it too. At least she raised no objection. Neither of us said a word.

The click of a door latch behind me broke the silence, and I felt her stiffen beneath my hand. The color drained from her face, and she stood quite still.

Nanny closed the kitchen door behind her and stepped out into the yard to draw some water from the well at the edge of the kitchen garden. My back was toward her, but I knew she was looking at us standing on either side of the low dividing fence.

Having drawn her pail of water from the old moss-covered well, Nanny walked back across the yard to the kitchen door, opened it, stepped inside with her pail of water, and closed the door behind her.

The color returned to Edith's cheeks, and she let out her breath in a long sigh.

I stopped stroking her hair and took both her hands in my own. "You know," I assured her gallantly and absolutely sincerely, "I think you're quite beautiful."

She looked at me wonderingly for a moment to see if I was serious, smiled shyly, turned, and ran back up the path to her house.

That's how I came to write a poem. I didn't see Edith for a couple of weeks, which gave me an opportunity to compose what I felt to be a fitting tribute to her.

I did not attend the village school, my education being provided for by other means, which was one reason I had not become acquainted with Edith before this. The man charged with guiding my introduction to the world of scholarship, however, had long since taught me to read—not an onerous task, as words had always fascinated me.

I composed a masterpiece that began: "The sun was shining on her hair," which still seems a rather good line. After this promising beginning, however, the poetry deteriorated rapidly.

Nevertheless, when I presented it to her across the fence upon our next meeting, Edith was ecstatic. She was visibly conscious of the honor done her and not at all critical of the work itself.

"A poem—about me!" she exclaimed, blushing to the roots of her hair. "No one has ever written a poem about me before—not in all my life."

I found her appreciation very gratifying.

I lost track of Edith as the years went by. Now, as I look back over a decade or two of war and uneasy peace and social upheaval that crumbled the class distinctions of those days, I recall that she grew up and married my cousin and, I have no reason to doubt, is living happily ever after.

The real hero of the incident is, of course, not Edith but Nanny. When she came upon the two of us reaching out tentatively to one another across a dividing fence, she went about her business of drawing water as if we were not there. She could have reprimanded us and made what was a moment of delicate beauty into something sordid. Worse yet, she could have laughed at us and made us appear ridiculous.

She did neither of these things. She made no comment of any kind, either then or later, to us or to anyone else. Her understanding and empathy were some of the reasons I loved her very much.

Later—much, much later—it was this quality of sensitivity and compassion that drew me irresistibly to a Savior who understands and enters into the thoughts and feelings of those who seek Him—whether in happiness or despair.

I am not vitally impressed—and I say this reverently—with the omnipotence that belongs to Heaven. I believe in it and accept it but am not intimately moved by it. It is the infinitely tender compassion of my Savior and of my heavenly Father that I find irresistible. It is this attribute of my Lord that I long for and earnestly covet for myself.

Edith has doubtless completely forgotten my poem, and Nanny is long gone, but this glowing memory of her shines brightly down the years—just one face of the many-faceted jewel of love.

WILD GEESE CALLING

Even when I was quite young, the sight of a flight of Canada geese high in the sky, flying in a wonderful "V" formation, heading toward their summer nesting ground on our small, ornamental lake at my home in Derbyshire, England, thrilled me beyond measure and, invariably, caused me to dissolve into tears. They were so—almost unbearably—beautiful.

"Well, now," began Macdonald, our old Scottish head gardener, rubbing his chin as he contemplated my latest question concerning nature and the living creatures that formed such a vital and important part of my experience as a country child. "Well, now," he repeated, looking into my face as I stood between his knees as he sat on the stone garden seat, taking a short break from his responsibilities of overseeing activities in the extensive gardens and hothouses adjacent to my home. "I don't know what kind of an explanation the scientists have as to how the birdies find their way here and there across the world, and I dinna care. It's my belief that the good Lord sends one of His angels, who flies ahead of the lead goose and shows him the way. How else could it be, I'm asking you?"

"Ah," I breathed, my eyes shining. I knew Macdonald would have an explanation.

"Nanny, Nanny! They're back! Our geese have come home. They're on the lake. I know they're the same daddy and mummy. Macdonald checked the rings he put on their legs. Isn't it wonderful? The angel showed them the way. Come on. Come and see them."

"Just for a minute or two, then, Boo. Then we must leave them alone for a while. They'll want to build their nest and get ready for the new babies."

I am not sure which of us was the most excited, me or the parent geese, but in a matter of not many days—days that seemed like weeks to me—the female goose was settled on a nest that, without a doubt, held the precious eggs that housed her new family.

Then, after a week or two of diligent care by both parents, who took turns keeping the eggs warm and turning them from time to time with their strong bills, we made the exciting discovery of broken pieces of eggshell floating on the water and unmistakable signs of activity in the nest on the tiny island in the middle of the lake.

Finally came the long-anticipated day when the babies made their debut, looking like a row of tiny, fluffy battleships paddling behind their parents with their surprisingly large feet, just as if they had been doing it all their lives—which, I suppose, they had—almost.

Nanny and I visited the lake every day as the enchanting little creatures grew and developed, admiring them and telling their parents how clever and beautiful they were. The parents got quite used to our presence, and seemed to appreciate our interest in and admiration of their delightful family.

I was particularly intrigued by the way the parent geese looked out for and cared for their young ones.

I watched the mother goose, who never seemed to take her eyes off her children while we were nearby, calling to them if they strayed farther from her than she felt to be safe.

"She loves them, doesn't she, Nanny?" I observed. "I expect that's what she's telling them. She wants them close to her all the time."

For some reason, watching the mother goose with her babies made me have funny feelings that I couldn't understand, feelings that made me want to cry. Nanny, who always knew what I was thinking and how I was feeling, looked at me and took my hand.

"Come, Boo," she said, "let's leave them alone for a while. Let's go back up to the house."

"All right, Nanny," I agreed. "But first, do you have time to just hold me for a minute? Will you, please?"

Nanny put her arms around me. "Stop shivering, Boo," she said. "I always have time to hold you when you need me."

The season progressed, and the goslings—that's what Macdonald called them; Nanny and I always called them goose babies—grew into mature young geese. Winter was coming, and soon they would be leaving for their other home across the sea. We knew they were getting ready to leave—to begin their dangerous journey across the Atlantic Ocean.

"They're getting ready to go, Nanny," I told her one evening as I was getting ready for bed. "I think they're just waiting for their angel to get here to show them the way. Do you think we could say a prayer for them so they will be safe and will come back again next year?"

"Yes, Boo. I think that's a good idea. Let's do that before you go to sleep."

We never did actually see the geese leave. They always seemed to do it at night.

In the morning, as I went down to the lake, a cold wind was blowing. Leaves were falling and beginning to carpet the ground beneath the trees, and a thin skin of ice was forming at the edge of the lake. The geese were gone.

I sat at the edge of the lake and looked at the empty nest on the little island. Except for the wind, it was very quiet. I cried a little—then I wiped my eyes and went home to tell Nanny.

Now, many years later, whenever I see a flight of geese, high in the windy sky, and hear them calling to each other, it always lifts my spirits and brings tears to my eyes. I still look for the angel flying ahead of the lead goose, showing the way.

I have never seen the angel. But, "scientific" explanations notwithstanding, just because you can't see something doesn't mean it isn't there.

BABY JESUS AND THE GARDENER'S DAUGHTER

The two of us stood before the simple Nativity scene in front of the high altar in the old Norman church beside the River Dove. We gazed with something approaching awe at the representation of the birthplace of the One to whom we prayed before we slept every night.

A rough wooden manger cradled a baby doll wrapped in "swaddling clothes," which we found, somewhat to our surprise, to be long strips of cloth bound tightly around the "baby." Life-size plaster figures of Mary, Joseph, and the shepherds guarded the manger, and in the background stood a lamb, a calf, and a donkey fashioned of the same material.

To Wendy and me, at 7 years old, it was a marvel.

It was cold in the unheated stone church. The warmth we had generated in our one-and-a-half-mile walk through the snow-covered North Derbyshire fields had dissipated. We could see our breath in the still air of the empty church, and we stamped our feet to stir the circulation in our toes.

The late-afternoon sun was giving way to dusk. Only a little light filtered through the stained-glass window behind the altar. It was time to be heading home. We placed the flowers we had brought for Him beside the "baby" and turned to go.

"I want to kiss Him," said Wendy, hopping on one foot and looking at me for reassurance. "Do you think it would be all right?"

I considered the suggestion for a moment, then nodded. "Yes, I think so," I told her. "After all, He *is* a baby."

Wendy knelt down, rather clumsily in her bulky winter clothing and snow boots. Tenderly she pressed her lips to the forehead of the baby doll.

"My, He *is* cold," she exclaimed. "Do you think I should leave Him my scarf?"

"No, you had better not," I advised her. "If you go home without it, your father will faint. You know how he is. He'll be sure you'll get pneumonia. Besides," I tried to reassure her, "I'm sure He'll be all right. I expect He's used to the cold by now."

"Yes, I expect you're right," she agreed. "Come on, let's go. I'll race you to the lych-gate!"

We left the church and trotted off in the twilight toward our homes. Most of the way we held hands, partly to provide mutual support and warmth, and partly because we were best friends.

Wendy, just six days younger than I, was the daughter of Angus Macdonald, our head gardener. The slightly built, blond-haired, blue-eyed little girl was the child of his old age, the light of the dour old Scotsman's life. Respected by all for his skill and integrity, feared by those who worked under him, the old man was putty in the tiny hands of his beloved last-born.

And because Wendy liked me and we were inseparable playmates, Macdonald like me too. I had unquestioned access to his domain. I was welcome to help myself to whatever I wanted in the extensive gardens and hothouses, and he always greeted me when our paths crossed—a courtesy seldom extended to anyone else.

Wendy and I spent a good deal of our time together in those days, especially in the summer months when she was released for a few weeks from the village school and my tutor was away on vacation.

On those warm and lazy days immediately following breakfast, I would run to the big windows of the day nursery, which looked out onto rolling velvety lawns. Invariably Wendy would be waiting for me on the grass. She would wave and beckon and jump up and down excitedly; sometimes in an excess of exhilaration she would turn a cartwheel or stand on her head.

"May I, Nanny?" I would ask.

"All right, but keep your eye on the sun. Don't be late for lunch."

Permission granted, we would be off together on a tour of the neighboring farms or across the moors to wade in the clear, cold streams, happy in our freedom and content in each other's company.

But in midwinter the moors were covered with ice and snow, and we couldn't go far afield in the short days.

Christmas Eve was the highlight of the holiday in those days. All the children—of family and servants alike—were permitted to stay up until midnight to attend the watch night at the church across the fields.

This particular year, as usual, the service was unbelievably magnificent. It wasn't just the organ music and the carols sung by the choir. The Nativity scene literally came alive for the special occasion. The manger held a real, live baby, and there were a real Mary and Joseph, real shepherds, and even a real calf, lamb, and donkey lying in the straw piled thickly on the flagged floor of the church.

But spectacular though it was, it did not stir me quite so deeply as that moment the previous day when just the two of us had knelt before the pretend Baby and offered Him our flowers.

I wanted to be with Wendy now, but I knew she would be with her parents in the body of the church. I was seated toward the front with my parents and sister on the cushioned seats in our family pew.

It didn't take Wendy and me long to find each other after the service. I asked permission to walk home with her family, who promised to deliver me at the house in short order, in one piece, and unfrozen. Then Wendy and I ran off happily over the crisp snow. Wendy chattered away, telling me of the new ice skates "Father Christmas" was almost sure to bring her before morning.

Father Christmas came through. He brought the skates. Wendy, however, never had a chance to use her long-awaited Christmas gift.

On the sixth day of the new year she died from what was known in those days as brain fever. Nowadays it would be called meningitis.

Two days after the funeral I was wandering through the kitchen gardens toward the hothouses when I came upon Macdonald sitting on a garden seat, alone in the cold. Since the onset of Wendy's brief illness he had scarcely moved and had spoken to no one.

He saw me approaching and raised his head. He had tears on his face. I had never seen a grown person cry before. He held his arms out to me, and I stumbled up to him. He took me on his lap and held me tightly against his rough tweed jacket as we cried together. Neither of us said a word.

It was terrifying and yet somehow comforting.

Nanny—a remarkably understanding woman who had spent all her adult life loving and caring for other people's children—didn't say much.

About a week later, however, as she watched me looking silently out of the nursery window at a lone robin pecking at a frozen holly bush, she said, "Boo, as long as you remember her, Wendy will never really be gone. She will always be there."

Although there have been many Christmases since that night, I have never forgotten the wonder of that pilgrimage by two 7 year olds through the snow-covered English fields to bring gifts to the Christ child.

THE VIEW FROM THE CHURCH TOWER

"I want to go to the church today, Mary," I told my sister when she arrived at my nursery door quite early that January morning. "I want to take some flowers for Wendy."

"All right, Boo," my sister, a year and a half older than my 7 years, agreed. "It's very cold, though, and snowing a bit. You must put your scarf and gloves on. And when you get the flowers from Macdonald, you'd better get chrysanthemums. Anything from the hothouses would freeze in a couple of minutes."

It took just a few minutes to collect a big bunch of small "Tom Thumb" chrysanthemums and some Michaelmas daisies, and Mary and I were on our way, trudging through the snow in our clumsy snow boots and taking turns holding the flowers in our mittened hands.

"Do you think she will like them, Mary?" I pressed my sister, anxiously evaluating my bouquet. "She does like purple, I know."

I still could not accept the fact that Wendy, my 7-year-old playmate and best friend, was dead, even though I knew she was lying in a small grave in the churchyard of St. Mary's Church at Marston-on-Dove, which was our immediate destination.

It didn't take us very long to traverse the one and a half miles from our home, Hoon Villa, through the snow-covered fields, following the now invisible footpath to the church. We could see the tall spire of the tenth-century Norman church in the distance, so the virtual absence of the footpath caused us no concern.

"Can we go up to the top of the tower first, Mary?" I requested. "It's so beautiful."

"All right," agreed my sister. "But you must promise that you won't cry. If you do, I won't take you again."

"All right, Mary," I assured her, without much conviction. Although she had threatened not to take me again if I cried, I knew she would.

Dear, practical Mary was endlessly patient with her strange little brother, whom she had christened "Boo" at birth, and "Boo" I remained, secure in the knowledge that, trial though I must have been at times, she really loved me.

We stomped the snow from our boots and lifted the heavy iron handle on the thick oak door that led to the winding stone stairway inside the tower of the 1100-year-old church.

There were lots of steps. I had often begun to count them, but always lost count about halfway up as I stopped to wonder at the huge bells in the bell loft with the ropes hanging down all the way to the floor of the church, where the bell ringers pulled on them to make the bells ring. When they were ringing the bells, we could hear them clearly at our house, almost two miles from the belfry. It was a curiously stirring sound, especially when they were ringing "changes," and often made me cry, which would surprise no one who was at all acquainted with me.

"The steps are all worn away, Mary," I observed. "They are hollowed out in their middles."

"Well," said Mary, assuming what I called the "schoolmarmish" expression, "that's because people have been climbing up and down these steps for more than a thousand years, Boo."

"Oh, Mary," I responded, "that's a very long time, isn't it?"

Mary made no reply. I think she felt that my observation warranted no response.

After a few minutes, panting and no longer feeling cold, we reached the top of the stairway and went out onto the rectangular platform just below the spire. It was enclosed by a low parapet.

"Now, Boo," admonished my sister sternly, "don't lean over the parapet, or—"

"I know, Mary," I interrupted her. "You won't bring me again."

"I wasn't going to say that," said Mary. "I was going to tell you that if you do lean over, you'll fall all the way down and go *splat* on the ground, all flat and horrid, like a squashed toad, with all your insides coming out."

"Oh, Mary," I implored, "don't. I won't. I promise. Will you hold my hand, please?"

We stood a safe distance from the parapet and gazed over the snow-covered and, to me, incredibly beautiful landscape. Directly below was the graveyard, where I knew my dear little friend had been lying for about a week now, and where so many of my grandparents, great-grandparents, and "ancestors" (Mary called them) lay too. The River Dove was a narrow, silver ribbon just beyond the graveyard, flowing gently between its now snow-covered banks.

Looking in the other direction, I knew that our house, a big gray stone pile, was there, but was hidden from view by the oak and elm trees surrounding it.

"Oh, Mary," I breathed. "It's so beautiful." Tears ran down my face and immediately felt cold upon my cheeks.

Mary looked at me but made no comment other than to say, "Yes, Boo, it is very beautiful."

I thought about Wendy and longed to hear her voice again. "I love you, Wendy," I told her.

"Come, Boo," said Mary. "It's time to go. Bring your flowers."

She didn't say any more, but she held my hand all the way down.

I thought somehow that Mary would have cried too, except that she was so old.

It had begun to snow again, very lightly. Nanny used to say, "It is the doves around Jesus' throne in heaven, fluttering their wings."

"I'll wait here, Boo," said Mary when we got to Wendy's little grave, "while you take her your flowers. Take your time. Give her my love."

We walked home together. The snow was falling faster now. Mary held my hand.

A PIECE OF CAKE

Aunt Bertha was a character out of a Victorian novel. In actual fact, however, she was neither Victorian nor my aunt. She was the sister of my former nanny, and the events that follow took place between the First and Second World Wars in a small village in Derbyshire, England.

I was 9 years old at the time, and I had not seen Aunt Bertha for several years.

Things had changed for my family since those first idyllic years when Nanny and I had conducted our mutual admiration society. We had met in the airy nursery on the second floor of the huge, rambling house where I was born. She had taken me from the doctor's arms, and for the first four years of my life I never spent a day away from her. She called me Boo. I was her boy, and she was my world.

I saw my parents regularly, of course. Every afternoon I was dressed in a fresh white shirt, blue velvet short pants, white socks, and patent leather shoes. Then I was taken downstairs to greet my parents—a tall, black-haired man who patted me kindly on the head and asked me if I was being a good boy, and a delicately pretty, auburn-haired woman who kissed me gravely on the cheek and hoped that I was well.

Nanny's idea of an afternoon off (which happened once a week) was to take me with her to her home in the village and show me off to her sister—Aunt Bertha. Aunt Bertha was two or three years younger than Nanny—which made her about 50 years old—but to me she appeared ageless. Time seemed to have forgotten Aunt Bertha. Or maybe, for her, time had stopped.

Aunt Bertha had been crossed in love. She had been an unusually attractive young girl with soft, dark hair and flashing black eyes, so it had been no surprise to anyone when she had announced her engagement to William Benson, an ambitious young farmer from a village three miles away. After all, she had no parents living, only her unmarried sister and a brother.

It was a surprise to many, however, when six weeks before the wedding day Will Benson broke off the engagement and proceeded to woo and marry Harriet Stone, six years his senior and not overly handsome, but heir to 300 acres of good land.

In similar situations Victorian young ladies fainted dead away, went into a decline, sickened, and died. Aunt Bertha did none of these things. She shed no visible tears. She merely announced her intention of never leaving the house again until her dying day, and she never did.

Oh, she stepped outside of the cheerful little cottage and puttered around in the flower garden in front, dutifully tending the phlox, delphiniums, and love-lies-bleeding that ran riot under the laburnum and cherry trees.

Her tall, spare figure was a familiar sight to the boys who crept through the hedge at the back of the house to steal apples from the orchard. "Out, you varmints!" she would demand. The boys acquired a healthy respect for the ashplant she would sling. Aunt Bertha, perhaps understandably, didn't like boys.

And Aunt Bertha didn't like me. For some reason, perhaps because Nanny worshipped me, and her older sister was her strength and stay, Aunt Bertha *loved* me. As far as Aunt Bertha was concerned, I could do no wrong—a very comfortable feeling for a very young and impressionable male.

Up the crooked wooden stairway we would go, into the apple loft, where the apples were all spread out on the floor, carefully separated by Aunt Bertha into their various categories—Baldwins, Northern greenings, and russets, with their rough-textured skin and sweet, nutty flavor.

We would sit companionably on an old newspaper on the floor, and Aunt Bertha would select an apple for me from the small pile of red-and-yellow-striped apples that she always referred to as "love apples." She would select one for herself, polish them both on her long, black apron, and we would sit there for a long while, chewing our apples, savoring the fascinating mingled odors of apples, dust, and mice. Hardly talking, just enjoying each other's company. In fact, I really preferred the russet apples, but I would have died rather than to have hinted such a thing to Aunt Bertha.

Following afternoon tea—homemade cake and cambric tea on the best blue willow-pattern china—Aunt Bertha would take me to see Monkey, the cat.

Aunt Bertha always had lots of cats. Since she could never bring herself to drown the kittens, cats were not in short supply, either in the house or in the outbuildings. Some of Aunt Bertha's cats, of course, suffered mishaps. Some wandered away, got lost, took up residence elsewhere, or were spirited away by Aunt Bertha's brother, Harry, a tall old man with a beard whom I seldom saw.

Monkey, however, was *the cat.* He lived in the old chicken house down near the orchard.

Aunt Bertha had no intention of Monkey's getting lost or stolen or run over. The other cats had to survive on milk and scraps and what they could catch, but Monkey was fed cream and liver and sometimes even fish. He had everything a cat could desire—except his freedom. Monkey was never allowed out of his pen.

Aunt Bertha and I would open the wire-netting window to Monkey's pen and scratch him under his chin. He enjoyed that. Then it would be time for Nanny and me to go back through the village, Nanny greeting her friends along the way.

Then suddenly, overnight, it seemed that everything was changed. Everything that made up my familiar world was swept away.

When Nanny tucked me into bed one night, it was all there. In the morning it was gone—swept away in the economic disaster that was breaking up estates and homes all over England—indeed, all over Europe.

Naturally, I understood little of what was taking place. All I knew was that the bottom had dropped out of my world. Nanny, with tears streaming down her face, kissed me, clung to me for a moment, and stepped into the carriage that was to take her and her wicker traveling trunk down into the village. It was the first time since I was born that she had ever gone anywhere without me. I have never felt so desperately alone as I felt right then.

Almost immediately everything familiar was sold or packed up, and we moved from the big country house into an apartment in town. A period of abject misery began, which was to last for what seemed like a very long time but was probably three or four years. From being the center of my small universe, I had become, I sensed, an additional and unwelcome responsibility at a very trying time.

Word came a couple of years later that Nanny was very sick. I was taken to her bedside just in time to kiss her goodbye. For some reason I was not permitted to "follow the coffin" to the churchyard in the field beside the River Dove.

I stayed in the city on the day of the funeral and went to school. I left my books on the bus that morning and was reprimanded four times in class for not paying attention.

A couple of years passed, and I was 9 when Mother had occasion to go to the village near our former estate. As it was a school holiday, she decided to take me with her.

We traveled by bus, and as we approached the familiar scenes from my early childhood, my heart began to thump, and tears came to my eyes.

After Mother had completed her business, she—inexplicably—announced her intention of paying a call on Miss Fern. Mother did not approve of my calling her Aunt Bertha—she considered this inappropriate.

As we opened the little wicket gate and walked up the familiar red-brick path—overgrown now with moss and weeds—to the front door, my throat was so constricted I could scarcely swallow.

Mother tapped on the door with the handle of her umbrella. After a brief interval the door opened, and Aunt Bertha appeared on the doorstep. The same Aunt Bertha, to be sure, but infinitely older, no longer upright, hair gray and face wrinkled, but wearing the same—or it seemed the same—black apron I remembered.

She gazed at us suspiciously at first, unbelieving. Then a light dawned in her eyes. She threw her arms around me and showered kisses on the top of my head. "It's Boo," she said unbelievingly, again and again, and tears ran down her cheeks and onto my hair.

She hardly seemed aware of my mother's presence, a highly unusual experience for Mother. A situation, nevertheless, that Mother lost no time in remedying, making clear that she considered such a display of emotion unseemly.

We were invited inside and—for me, at least—the years rolled away as if they had never been. I was back in the apple loft again, surrounded by love and security.

"You'll stay for tea, won't you?" inquired Aunt Bertha eagerly, bustling around to lay the table with the dear, familiar blue willow-pattern china. "I've got some cake," she added anxiously, sensing my mother's hesitation as she glanced around at the dust on the furniture, the cats asleep on the hearth rug, and the general air of dishevelment that had replaced the previous immaculateness of the cottage.

"No, Bertha," said my mother firmly. "Thank you, but I don't believe we will. I have a little more business to take care of before we get our bus."

Aunt Bertha's face crumpled, the light in her eyes went out, and tears filled them. She slowly put the plate that she was polishing with her apron back on the table and turned away.

I believe at that moment I could have cheerfully struck my mother. Desperately I racked my brain to devise some way to shield Aunt Bertha from this monstrous hurt. I knew that where my mother was concerned, pleading would be worse than useless.

"Well, goodbye, Bertha," said Mother brightly. "Come, Arthur."

Frantically I fumbled in my pocket for my bus ticket, dropped it on the floor behind the door, kissed Aunt Bertha hurriedly, and followed Mother out the door, leaving Aunt Bertha standing in the doorway, stock-still, as if she were turned to stone.

"Why wouldn't you stay for tea, Mother?" I asked as soon as we were out of earshot.

"Arthur!" said Mother indignantly. "Have you taken leave of your senses? Didn't you see how dirty the house was? The whole place smelled of cats. Why, Bertha herself wasn't really clean. And she used to be so immaculate before Nanny and Harry died."

Now was the time. I fumbled in my pocket. "Mother," I said with conviction, "I've lost my bus ticket. I must have dropped it at Aunt Bertha's."

"Really, Arthur!" Mother cried irritably. "Go and look for it, then, and be quick about it. Whatever is wrong with you today? For a big boy, you're acting most strangely. Hurry up. I'll wait in the post office for you."

Running back to the cottage as quickly as I could, I arrived breathless on the doorstep and knocked urgently on the door. Aunt Bertha opened the door and took me in her arms. She had been crying.

"Aunt Bertha," I said, "I dropped my bus ticket, so I came back for it. Can I have a piece of cake?"

Ten minutes later I wiped the crumbs from my mouth and waved goodbye to Aunt Bertha, who was smiling through her tears. Clutching my bus ticket in my hand, I ran back to meet the tirade I knew I could expect from Mother.

I never saw Aunt Bertha again. She died three months later and was buried beside her sister and brother in the churchyard beside the river. I wasn't permitted to attend the funeral. Mother represented the family at the graveside. But I was permitted to send a small bouquet of flowers. On the card it said: "To Aunt Bertha, with love, from Boo."

GYPSY GIRL

I don't suppose Mr. Richards set out to be deliberately sadistic. I think it just came naturally to him. It was part of his disposition and a natural reaction to his discontent with his job and his dislike of boys in general.

It was, nevertheless, unfortunate for me that during my mercifully brief sojourn in his classroom while awaiting admission to a private school, he was, for six hours, five days a week, in charge of my person.

I made very sure, however, that he never for a moment had charge of my soul.

At 9 years old I believed myself, perhaps not without reason, to be more intelligent than he. Mr. Richards, already less than well-disposed toward me—regarding me as an interloper and a representative of a social class for which he nurtured a pathological hatred—sensed my evaluation of his capabilities and proceeded to work on my notion of self-worth.

Mr. Richards was a lifelong member of the Socialist Party and had taught for 26 years at St. John's Council School, the village school near my home in northern England. It catered to the children of the local farmworkers and rural artisans, and, inexplicably, my parents had consigned me here until an opening at an alternative establishment materialized.

Pop Richards, as he was generally known by his students, was not physically abusive. He was not a bully, except in the emotional sense. He confined his efforts at student destruction to tongue-lashings, bitter sarcasm, and psychological humiliation.

This was fortunate for me. Though tall for my age, I was slightly built and, I suppose, being very fair-skinned and having light-blond hair, somewhat delicate-looking—a factor that Pop lost no time in seeking to use to his advantage.

Very quickly I realized which way the wind blew. I knew Pop would never actually strike me, and I immediately assured him—though not to his face—that when it came to wars of words, young though I was, he had met his Waterloo.

At first, of course, I was a nine days' wonder. I was dressed differently from the rest of the pupils, I spoke differently, and I behaved differently.

The boys in the class (it was a coeducational school) initially regarded me with curiosity and some amusement. The girls, however, were at first also curious, then delighted with me. Behaving as I had been brought up to behave, and seeing no valid reason to change my behavior to suit my surroundings, I picked up their books, opened doors for them, allowed them to be seated in the shared desks first, and, in general, extended to them the courtesies to which, in my world, they were by nature entitled. They loved it. The boys, needless to say, cast a jaundiced eye upon this "unmanly" behavior.

Also, having had the advantage of a private tutor since I was 5 years old, I was academically ahead of the rest of the class, which did not tend to endear me to the male population. While they affected to disdain achievement in schoolwork, undeniably my ascendancy still rankled.

However, I had never been concerned about "making friends and influencing people," so, by and large, I held my own as Pop Richards and I glowered at each other daily from the front row seat he had assigned me so he could "keep an eye on me."

One week after my introduction to the advantages of public education, Esme turned up, and Pop Richards, putting an unlikely one and one together, saw his chance to, if not destroy, at least maul me badly.

Blessed with the unlikely name of Esme Dainty, the newcomer was a young gypsy girl from the encampment of gypsies newly arrived on the outskirts of the village for an indefinite stay on their way to the annual Appleton Horse Fair.

About 10 years old, the newcomer was no stranger to many of the children, as she had attended school before for brief periods during her family's periodic sojourns in the neighborhood.

She was greeted in a somewhat ribald fashion by her classmates: "Hello, Esme; back again." "Watcher, gyppo; steal any 'osses lately?" and similar welcoming comments.

Esme made no reply. She just stood there in her ragged dress and bare feet, waiting to be told what to do next.

Pop lost no time in implementing his plan of campaign. "Well, Esme," he boomed, rubbing his hands, "you're back. Welcome, my little bird of passage. Come, I have just the spot. I saved it just for you. You may sit up front here in this double desk alongside Mr. Superior."

He led the girl to the front of the room and indicated the empty seat next to mine. "This is a special seat, Esme, my girl," he purred. "Not just any old body can sit here."

He stepped up to the desk and thrust his face close to mine. "Take care of the young lady, now, boy," he admonished me. "Don't forget your manners."

He backed off. I silently summed up the situation while the child next to me, obviously intimidated, nervously twisted her dress between her slender brown fingers.

As soon as our tormentor had perforce returned to assigning the work for the period, I took the opportunity to steal a glance at my seatmate, who was sitting very straight, with her hands in her lap, being careful not to touch me.

She was a slightly built child, with long, somewhat greasy black hair, very dark eyes, a small, delicate mouth, and the olive skin that was an indication of her Romany heritage.

Unfortunately, she was not very clean. To put it bluntly, she was very dirty. She had an aura that, as nearly as I could determine, was compounded of dirt, wood smoke, and horses, and, I observed unhappily, her nose was running copiously.

I knew that Pop Richards was watching us covertly, enjoying every minute of the tableau he had devised. I ignored him.

"Esme," I said, turning toward her and proffering my white handkerchief, "would you like to use my handkerchief—for your nose?"

The girl jumped, gave me a look reminiscent of a startled animal, took the proffered handkerchief, and applied it to her nose with dubious results.

That may not have done much good, I thought, *but at least she took it and didn't burst into tears or run out of the room or anything.*

Esme completed her nose and face polishing operation and, with a shy smile, attempted to return the handkerchief. I was a bit unprepared for this.

"No, you keep it," I told her, "in case you need it again."

She looked at me, unbelieving, then looked at the handkerchief, cradling it in her hands as if it were the Holy Grail. Then she smiled again, wordless, and quickly tucked it into the neck of her dress.

That was the beginning of an unusual but rewarding friendship. It was a couple of days before the timid little girl opened up and began to talk to me. When she did, I found her to be an intelligent and fascinating, though unsophisticated, companion.

Pop couldn't disguise his disappointment over the failure of his plan, but after a number of unsuccessful attempts to discomfit us, he left us severely alone. I did my best to protect the little gypsy girl from the inevitable attempts on the part of her classmates to embarrass her, and took pains to emphasize that I enjoyed her company.

I walked her home every day, leaving her at the entrance to her encampment—a collection of caravans, horses, dogs, and innumerable small children in various states of undress. Gypsy men, and some women, sat on the steps of some of the caravans or tended fires on which they were usually cooking savory-smelling stews.

With sympathetic attention Esme blossomed. She became much less introverted—at least with me—and she began to take an interest in her appearance.

She washed herself, found a semi-clean dress that, for reasons I never fathomed, was much longer at the back than at the front, and did her best, in a good deal less than ideal circumstances, to make herself presentable.

She smiled shyly when I complimented her sincerely upon her appearance. "Esme, you look so nice," I told her as we made our way to school.

She blushed furiously when some of the boys whistled as we entered the school yard. She blushed again when Pop Richards commented as we took our seats, "Wonderful what a new boyfriend will do for a girl, isn't it, gang?"

Some of the boys laughed dutifully. Some were silent. Even though most still regarded me as pretty weird, some realized that I had Pop Richards' measure, and they respected me for that.

"Esme," I began as we walked home from school one afternoon, "did you know that you have beautiful hair?"

She looked at me wonderingly, blushed, and fingered the long hair that reached almost to her waist.

"If it was washed and brushed, it would look absolutely lovely," I ventured.

Esme looked at me, tears forming in her eyes. "Where could I? What could I . . ." she faltered.

I set down her books, took her hands, and broke in: "Tomorrow; you wait. I've got a great idea." I refused to elaborate and left her, excited and puzzled, at the gate of the encampment.

The following day I brought a paper sack to school, which I hid in my desk, refusing to let Esme see—or even feel—its contents. "Wait until after school," I told her. "It's for you."

After school I grabbed our books and the mysterious sack, took Esme's hand, and led her off in a different direction from the one we usually took.

"Where are we going?" she demanded. "Where are you taking me?"

"You'll see" was all I would tell her.

After a few minutes we reached the small river that flowed around two sides of the encampment, although several fields distant. I knelt down on the grass, opened the sack, and tipped out the contents.

Esme couldn't believe her eyes: a hairbrush, a tube of shampoo, a towel, and three other items that I quickly hid for a surprise for later. All these treasures I had acquired from the dressing room of my 10-year-old sister. She had plenty more and would not miss them, I told myself. I knew she readily would have given me whatever I asked for, but I didn't want to have to explain why I wanted them.

"What—what are you going to do?" stammered Esme, understandably bewildered.

"We're going to wash your hair," I told her excitedly. "In the river."

We approached the river's edge at a shallow spot I had previously selected. "Kneel down," I instructed Esme, "and stick your head in the water. I know it's supposed to be hot water, but we haven't got any, and this stuff is supposed to work in cold water, anyway."

Esme obediently dipped her head in the stream and began to splash water onto her hair. Between us we thoroughly shampooed and rinsed her long tresses until they looked—and smelled—clean and fragrant.

"My, it's cold." She shivered, stepping onto the bank. "But my hair feels wonderful."

"It looks lovely, too," I assured her. "Just wait till you see what else I've got for you. Shut your eyes and open your hands."

In her hands I placed the two long ribbons I had selected from my sister's overflowing ribbon drawer—one green-striped and one pure white. Esme opened her eyes and looked at the ribbons. Her beautiful dark eyes filled with tears. She didn't say a word.

"Now," I began in an effort to break the tension, "I'm no expert, but I'll try to show you how to fix the ribbons in your hair. Anyway, you're probably better at it than I am."

With some difficulty, as we were equally inexperienced, we tied the green ribbon into Esme's rapidly drying hair. She posed against a tree so that I could evaluate the effect.

"You are unbelievably beautiful," I told her. "Stay there." I felt like a conjurer as I produced the final item I had brought, courtesy, in absentia, of my sister, Mary.

Esme gazed into the small hand mirror for a long moment, sighed deeply, then impulsively threw her arms around me and kissed me soundly.

"Thank you," I said, a bit breathless. "I liked that." I handed her the bag with all the equipment. "These are for you."

"To keep?" she wondered, holding the paper sack to her chest. "Thank you."

Our triumphal entry into the classroom the following morning fulfilled all my expectations. Esme's long black hair was brushed and shining. She had tied the white ribbon around it about halfway down, and she looked . . . I guess radiant is the word.

Inevitably and, I think, happily, there were some whistles, but for once Pop Richards held his tongue. He looked at us—first at Esme, then at me—closed his mouth (which had dropped open) with a snap, and took his place at his desk without a word.

By this time I was increasingly worried about how I was to tell Esme that I wouldn't be at the school much longer. In a few short weeks I had come to feel as if we were hardly two separate people anymore.

As it turned out, my worries were groundless. I set out for school one morning and headed for the gypsy encampment as usual to meet Esme. On the way I encountered a farmhand on his way to his work in the fields. He stopped and hailed me, eyeing me quizzically. "I shouldn't bother going to meet your little friend, lad," he said, not unkindly. "They've gone. The gypos left last night."

"What do you mean, they're gone?" I demanded. "Where are they?"

"Who knows?" responded the laborer. "'Eadin' for Appleton Fair eventually, I'll be bound. 'Oss tradin' time afore long."

I left him and continued toward the entrance to the encampment. The gate was swinging open. There was litter of all sorts strewn over the field. Remnants of campfires, cold now, marked where the cooking pits had been. Not a sign of life—nor a sound.

I followed the wheel tracks out through the gate and headed toward the school. When I got there, though I was early, I went into the classroom and sat down at our desk. The bell rang, and the others came in followed by Pop Richards. No one spoke to me.

Mr. Richards looked at me with something akin to compassion. "If you want to go and sit in that single desk in the back," he said, "that will be all right."

I DIDN'T EVEN KNOW HER NUMBER

She had long, shining black hair and the biggest brown eyes I had ever seen. She was, of course, very intelligent and played the piano like an angel (although, I suppose, that's really a harp, isn't it?). Her name was Monika.

At 9 years old I happened to be between a tutor and a boarding school. My tutor (ex-tutor, at this point) had taken himself off to Austria on a mountain-climbing vacation, and the boarding school at which I had been enrolled lacked three months until term time.

My parents, firm believers in unremitting industry—at least for me—had contrived to enroll me in a program for gifted children that convened in the city closest to our country home in Derbyshire, England. This would be marvelous for me, I was assured. I would get used to meeting and interacting with other children, and my brain would have no opportunity to go rusty in the interim period before I began to enjoy the inestimable advantages of the exclusive boarding school at which I had been enrolled before I was born.

I didn't say anything. For one thing, no one was asking, and by this stage in my life I was already a confirmed fatalist.

But actually, it was very different from my expectations. It was quite unlike what I had imagined, in my total lack of experience, an ordinary school to be. The student body, contrary to the common practice, was comprised of both boys and girls, and the age range was wide, from about 7 years old to one boy of 15.

The students were, without exception, highly intelligent, and each had a specialty—almost an obsession, I observed—in which he or she excelled. The general curriculum, which everyone, including me, found not terribly challenging, was not taken too seriously by anyone, and each of us spent most of our time engaging in the specialty of our choice.

There seemed to be plenty of teachers around. They were unobtrusive but were available to anyone who felt a need for advice or instruction or just wanted to chat.

The kids mostly worked alone or in pairs, and there wasn't much of the interaction with which I had been threatened. I kind of liked the setup.

I met Monika the second day I was there. For some reason she registered a day late and came in with her parents just as we were beginning work at around 9:30 in the morning. Her father paused and, in German-accented English, asked me—as I happened to be near the door—the whereabouts of the music studio.

Her father and mother went into the office alone to sign papers and shell out money, I suppose, and Monika sat down near me to wait for them. She looked nervous, I thought, so being a kindhearted sort of kid, I engaged her in conversation and tried to put her at ease. Besides, I wanted to get a good look at her. I thought she was the most beautiful girl I had ever seen.

In addition to the aforementioned eyes and hair, she had beautiful hands with long, slender, tapered fingers. She spoke softly with what to me was a delightful European accent. Always susceptible to beauty, I was immediately enchanted. School, I decided, was a great place after all. Why hadn't I been afforded these marvelous experiences before?

The inconceivable had taken place: my parents were absolutely right. With a heart overflowing with love and gratitude, I forgave them everything.

Monika and I quickly became inseparable. I listened to her play the piano (her specialty), and she read the poetry and prose I had been inspired to produce (my specialty). Some of the poems were even about her. She liked that, and I liked her liking it.

What made things even better was that my sainted parents had arranged lodgings for me in town for the duration of my stay at the school, and these lodgings (Heaven was on my side; I began to say my prayers regularly again) happened to be just down the avenue from where Monika lived with her father, who was a research executive temporarily with the Rolls-Royce Company, and her mother, who stayed home keeping things beautiful for her adored husband and only daughter.

The people with whom I was lodging had never had such an unobtrusive lodger. When not in school, I spent most of my time at Monika's house. I would, of course, walk her home (somebody had to carry her music) and would invariably be urged to stay and eat and socialize for a while. I wasn't hard to persuade. I just called my lodgings to report my whereabouts, and sort of took up residence.

Looking back, I suspect that Monika's father, Herr Pickering, regarded me with amused tolerance. His wife, however, made no secret of the fact that she thought I was wonderful. Having long held this opinion myself, I warmed to her immediately.

She would gaze at Monika and me sitting on the step engrossed in some activity or other with our heads, one very blond, the other very dark, close together, and would make little clucking noises with her tongue. Sometimes her eyes would fill with tears, and she would come over and put her arms around the two of us.

I think she had some sort of dream of our eventually rearing a line of progeny that would be sort of a cross between Shakespeare and Paderewski. Without having any clear idea of what it entailed, Monika and I thought this a marvelous idea.

But it was not to be. As I said, I was already a fatalist. I guess I knew all along that the idyll couldn't last. Nothing ever had.

Just before the program closed for the end of term, Monika's father was suddenly recalled by his parent firm in Hamburg, Germany. There was a lot of animated and sometimes tearful discussion in the household as to whether they should go or not. (The family was Jewish, and strange stories were filtering out of Europe about that time.) But in the end, disciplined, responsible Herr Pickering decided it was his duty to return with his family to his homeland.

Monika and I were heartbroken. We never got to celebrate her eleventh birthday together, as we had planned. I don't suppose she ever received the little necklace I sent her for her birthday. We vowed to write, and I did. I got one letter.

The last news I had of Monika and her family came through another German family that had elected to remain in England. They said the Pickerings were last heard of in a place called Bergen-Belsen. That was Monika's last address.

I couldn't write to her there. I didn't even know her number.

ALWAYS THERE WAS SOMEONE

I knew—at least I had been assured—that it was a very good school. It was very old. It was established in the time of Edward VI, who was its patron. My father had been a student there, as had my grandfather, his father, and his father before him. All of which left me quite unimpressed.

The only glimmer of hope on the horizon that I could perceive as I climbed reluctantly out of the car and stood in front of the undeniably imposing gray stone cluster of buildings that comprised the school complex were my father's words as we had taken our leave of each other on the steps of my home some miles away: "Cheer up, old chap. You will be home for the holidays, and, you know, it won't be forever."

Someone came out of the building and proceeded to help Morrison unload my luggage from the car and carry it inside. The chauffeur stepped forward, touched his cap, and shook my hand. "Goodbye, Master Amott [my middle name]. Good luck."

I started up the steps to the administration building. I felt for all the world as if I was embarking on a prison sentence—five years to life or somewhere in there. I was mildly surprised to see no handcuffs around my wrists.

The whole place seemed to be swarming with boys—boys of all ages, sizes, and complexions. I had never seen so many people in one place at one time. They all appeared to be shouting to one another at the tops of their voices. I found them singularly unattractive and profoundly depressing.

A boy somewhat older than I—clad, like me, in the uniform prescribed in the school handbook—appeared as if by magic and motioned me to follow him. He was evidently some sort of minor official. (I was as yet unacquainted with the prefect system common to English preparatory and public schools.) One of his responsibilities, apparently, was to orient new boys and "show them the ropes," as he put it. (If he had handed me one right then, I could have put it to good use, I mused.)

The dormitory to which I was assigned was even worse than I had anticipated. The building, although architecturally imposing, originally a mansion built for some royal favorite or other, had been adapted many years previously for use as a boys' boarding school. The dormitories, like the rest of the accommodations, graphically emphasized the tremendous contrast between the astronomical fees charged and the facilities provided. The theory was that austerity, along with harsh discipline, was character-building. I didn't buy this concept, although I could see the benefit of the system from the point of view of profitability.

At home I had been surrounded by beauty, space, elegance, and, most important of all, solitude.

I could, with difficulty, tolerate the iron bedsteads and cramped and primitive facilities. The worst aspect of the whole situation for me—conditioned from birth to conducting my life on a solitary basis—was the horrifying realization that I could at no time expect to be alone.

I met my fellow inmates soon enough. My initial impression of them as singularly lacking in intelligence and sensitivity was reinforced as I observed that most of them appeared to be enjoying the situation. The "old-timers," indeed, even freely admitted that they were glad to be back. In all fairness, there were some, I am sure, who were no more favorably impressed with boarding school and dormitory life than I, but at that time I was in no condition to be selective in my judgment.

I tried to concentrate on my father's words: "It won't be forever." It had been three hours since my arrival, and already I had been there forever.

The customary ("traditional," I was assured) hazing before retiring for the night established the pattern. It was going to be me against them, and I determined that, even if I couldn't win, I would die rather than surrender.

Any form of violence had always been abhorrent to me. Nevertheless, faced with invasion of sorts of my person, I reacted immediately and with a violence of which I didn't know I was capable. Not one of those little hooligans was going to lay a finger on me if I could help it.

In a sort of hysteria, I suppose, I seized a piece from one of the as yet unassembled beds that happened to be within my reach and struck with all my strength the unfortunate boy who had been deputed to do the hazing.

The encounter put him in the school infirmary with a severe concussion and put me in the housemaster's office.

The good thing that emerged from the encounter from my point of view was that, from then on, the other boys left me severely alone. (They probably, perhaps not unreasonably, felt I had murderous intent.)

I have been particularly fortunate, throughout my life, to have the presence of someone in times of severe stress who was understanding and supportive. In my earlier, pre-boarding school days, my nanny, a particularly sensitive, understanding woman, had been my lifeline. There had been Wendy, and Monika, even Peggy, my cat.

Now, in this, to me, totally intolerable situation, I miraculously discovered twofold support. To my immense surprise, Mr. Hanmer, my housemaster—while he was certainly not easy on me, neither at this initial confrontation nor on the several subsequent occasions I was required to appear before him for disciplinary reasons—was amazingly understanding. His most memorable advice to me, which came a good deal later, was: "At least try and look as if you're conforming, there's a good chap." Somewhat to my surprise, because I must have caused him considerable vexation, he seemed to like me. Certainly I liked him. Anyone who had a daughter like Pamela had to be a very decent sort of fellow.

It was customary, in an effort to provide some sort of normalcy in our regimented life, for the housemasters to invite the boys in their house, individually, or, if two were close friends, in pairs, to their homes once or twice a term for tea, cakes, and conversation, and exposure to the family life from which they had been separated.

My first visit to the Hanmer home took place, providentially, perhaps, at a very low point in my first term. Everything looked very black to me at that time. I was even beginning to think that not living at all would be better than the way things were. I was 9 years old.

I don't remember clearly what Mrs. Hanmer looked like. She hovered in the background, dispensing tea and ginger snaps. (At least I think they may have been ginger snaps. I was hardly aware of what I was eating.)

It was like staggering through a desert and finally stumbling across an oasis. Here were beauty, quietness, music, and sensitivity. It was all I could do to prevent myself from bursting into tears.

Best of all, of course, there was Pamela. Pamela was also 9 years old, but she acted older. I suppose, being the housemaster's daughter, she was used to helping entertain boys. At any rate, she appeared to be completely at ease, and actually seemed to be genuinely interested in what I had to say.

I thought she was quite beautiful. She had brown eyes, long brown hair, and a delightful heart-shaped face that made my heart turn over. She was wearing a blue, flowered dress with short sleeves. (I hadn't seen anybody in a dress for ages.) I was totally enchanted. She talked to me. She asked me about my home, about my family, about what I was interested in. She even volunteered to play the piano for me. I thought I would die of happiness.

The visit ended, but not the relationship. Pamela and I became close friends. Whenever our free time coincided, we would take long walks together. She was as enchanted with nature as I was. She loved music and art as much as I did. She understood immediately why I hated wearing the school uniform we were admonished to wear with pride. She knew instinctively why I consistently refused to take part in singing the school song at assembly. (The words were unbelievably stupid, the music matched the words, and I had absolutely no intention of pledging lifelong allegiance to an institution that meant less than nothing to me.)

She was not disgusted because I felt sports to be a juvenile waste of time, and wasn't horrified because I could not possibly care less who won the interschool cricket match that assumed so much importance in so many minds. She appreciated my evaluation of the school Officer Cadet Training Unit—to which we all arbitrarily belonged—as silly little boys playing at soldiers.

She was beautiful. She was perfect, and she was my salvation.

English schoolgirls tend to be sent away to boarding school a year or two later than their brothers, so Pamela didn't have to go to her boarding school until she was 11 years old.

The day before she left, with the connivance of her father, I wrangled permission to skip all my classes for the day, and Pamela and I took a picnic provided by her mother and hiked to a spot about four or five miles distant with the unlikely name of Winkfield. It was springtime, and the bluebells were in full bloom. We climbed to a vantage point where we could see for several miles. It was a clear, sunny day with a light breeze.

As far as we could see, the whole earth was a carpet of shimmering blue. The breeze stirred the flowers, and they looked like a marvelous, rippling ocean. They reminded me of an Aubusson carpet in the morning room at home, except that this carpet was alive and moving.

We were breathing hard from the climb. We stood and looked and looked. We held each other's hands, and the tears rolled down our faces and splashed onto the wonderful blue carpet at our feet.

We stood there for a long time, and we didn't say a word. Then we turned and, still hand in hand, walked back down the hill and headed toward the school.

A SOFT FLAME OF HEATHER

She was an astonishingly beautiful child. Her hair was long and silky and jet-black like my father's, and her eyes were a very deep blue, almost violet. She had the longest eyelashes I had ever seen—except on a horse—and they were black and silky like her hair. When she looked down, they cast a shadow on her suntanned cheeks. She wore a short, blue dress, torn in several places but clean, and her feet were bare.

We observed one another for some moments—a little like two cats sizing each other up prior to deciding whether to fight or to be friends. She eyed me covertly from beneath lowered lashes. I regarded her openly, aware of my superior position as a male and heir to the big house and the land that surrounded us.

"Hello. What's your name?"

"Fiona."

"And how old are you?"

"Seven."

The preliminaries having been exhausted, the conversation temporarily languished. Having met very few people in her short life, she was quite shy.

Her initial shyness, however, soon wore off, overcome by a natural curiosity.

"I know where you come from," she volunteered. And, after a pause, "You're from the big house. What's your name?"

She had a soft, silvery voice, and I couldn't decide whether she was English or Scottish. Her speech carried hints of both dialects, not uncommon in the border country.

"Are you English or Scottish?" I demanded.

For some reason she laughed at this. "I don't know," she confessed.

"My father's the shepherd, you know—he's Scottish, but my mother, she's English."

"Anyway," I assured her, gallantly and absolutely sincerely, "I think you're quite beautiful."

She looked at me gravely for a moment to see if I was serious, and then she began to giggle at me softly.

"Have you always lived here?" I asked her.

"Ever since I was born," she assured me. Then, knitting her brows in a frown, she stated, "I've got to go now. My faither'll be waiting on his lunch."

I noticed for the first time that she was carrying a bundle tied up in a big, white kerchief. She stopped at the top of the rise to negotiate some rocks and turned and waved her hand. Then she was gone.

I didn't see her again for several days. I thought about her a lot, though. Essentially a solitary child, I spent a great deal of my time when not in school wandering over the moorland surrounding my home, my only companions the sheep that nibbled the short, wiry grass that grew between the outcropping rocks. The heather brought her to my mind because it was so nearly the color of her eyes.

My mother didn't really approve of my "wandering barefoot over hill and dale like a gypsy," though what harm she thought I might come to I could never imagine. But then I rarely did understand my mother—nor she me, I suspect.

It was my father to whom I was closest. A number of years older than my mother, he was a tall, handsome man with black hair and a big mustache. He was good-natured and friendly, and his ready smile and lively sense of humor endeared him to everyone. I admired and worshipped him.

He was a busy man, most of his days being occupied in overseeing the activities on the considerable acreage that surrounded the house. Nevertheless, he spent as much time with me as he could, and the hours we spent together were the high points of my days. My father was an ardent nature lover and a worshipper of beauty in all its forms; these enthusiasms he passed on to me.

We would tramp the moors until he sensed that I was tiring, whereupon he would declare vehemently that he "couldn't walk another step," and we would fling ourselves down on the heather and rest and talk. He would point out to me the beauty of the clouds or the haze on the distant hills. We would listen to the purling of the many streams that flowed, clear and cold, over the rocks, and exclaim over the perfection of the tiny wildflowers that bloomed everywhere on the relatively barren moorland.

Under his tutelage, the seemingly featureless landscape took on a beauty that enchanted me. When launched on his favorite subject—beauty and the pursuit of the same—my father, not normally a talkative man, became quite eloquent. I remember a former nursemaid I had when I was younger saying of him, "The master can charm a bird out of a tree, when he's a mind."

The next time I saw Fiona was when I was engaged in a "bird's-nesting" expedition—it being the spring of the year. I had been "conditioned" by my father—in the matter of birds' nests—to "look and admire, but not touch." The word picture my father drew for me of a moorland bereft of birds—silent and insect-ridden—was not really a necessary deterrent. I had no desire to take or to destroy. I was content to gaze in wonder at the perfection of the nests of the wild birds that frequented the vicinity. I desired no more than to look at the tiny eggs clustered in the nest, to admire their beauty of shape and color. I was not a collector by nature. I needed only to see. I stored up pictures in my mind to be taken out later at will so as to recapture the thrill of their beauty.

I had spent an hour or so scrambling over the rocks and wading the streams, and had finally come upon a real discovery. I had stumbled across the nest of a reed warbler. The hen had darted away at my approach, and I was standing ankle deep in the icy water of the stream, oblivious of the cold, gazing with something approaching awe at the incredibly beautiful olive-green eggs, when I heard what sounded like a suppressed giggle. Looking up from the nest, I saw Fiona standing a few feet from me, half hidden by an outcrop of rock, watching me. Her hair was blown half across her face by the spring breeze, and she held one hand to her mouth to stifle her giggles.

I looked up with mixed feelings. I didn't know whether to be annoyed because she was watching me and disturbing my solitude or to be pleased at meeting her again. Finally, my pleasure at seeing her again overcame my initial startled surprise, and I voluntarily smiled at her.

This time she spoke first. "What're you looking at?" she inquired. "Can I come across at the burn and have a look at it?"

"It's a reed warbler's nest," I told her excitedly. "With eggs in it. Come on across, then, but be quick. I don't want to keep the hen off the eggs much longer."

She waded across the stream and crouched down beside me over the nest. The breeze blew strands of her hair across my face, and I decided that she smelled like a mixture of fresh, sweet hay and heather. We concluded our admiration of the eggs and wandered on in search of further discoveries. This was the first of many expeditions together.

Frequently I would set out on a tour of inspection of my favorite moorland haunts, only to find Fiona waiting for me in a half-hidden spot out of sight of both our homes. I soon discovered that she loved the moors and the creatures that lived there no less than I did, and in some areas her knowledge of the ways of the wild things surpassed my own.

My solitary expeditions, which previously I had found totally satisfying, no longer formed the pattern of my days. My day did not really begin until I reached the place where Fiona was waiting for me. Hand in hand we would wander over the—to a stranger—trackless moor, which to us was completely familiar and beloved.

Sometimes we would talk. She would tell me of her home—of her father, the shepherd, and of her mother, and of the lambs she helped to care for when they were either orphaned or abandoned by their mothers. She was always particularly tender when she spoke of the orphaned lambs, sometimes even to the point of tears. At other times we would be silent, at one with the natural beauty surrounding us and content in each other's company.

Spring gave way to summer, and the days grew warm. The wild bees—"mossy toddlers," Fiona called them—murmured in the heather, and the dry stone walls that served as hedgerows on the moor were covered in places with honeysuckle and wild roses. Even the water in the moorland streams became relatively warm, and the speckled trout floated languidly just beneath the surface.

It was Fiona's idea that we should find a deep hole and go swimming.

"Where will we find a place deep enough?" I objected. "I don't know of anywhere where the water's more than three feet deep."

"I know a place," declared Fiona confidently. "Come on." She took my hand, and we set off at a run across the moor, heading toward where one of the bigger streams angled toward a sizable outcrop of limestone rock.

We arrived breathless at a spot where the stream flowed rapidly around the base of the biggest rock when Fiona abruptly called a halt. "Stop!" she ordered. "Shut your eyes. I've got a surprise for you."

Taking my hand in one of hers and covering my eyes with her other hand so I couldn't "peek," she led me around the big rock and stopped. The sound of the water was suddenly louder with a sort of echo to it I hadn't heard before.

"There!" she said triumphantly in her high, clear voice. "You can look now."

She took my hand from my eyes, and I gazed in amazement. I had thought I knew the moors pretty well, but I had never been here before. The stream made its way around the base of the huge rock and then suddenly dropped five or six feet over a shelf into a rocky basin about 12 feet in diameter, from which it dropped again several more feet and disappeared from view into an underground cavern.

I could scarcely believe my eyes. Fiona was ecstatic with the success of her "surprise." She sat on the ground and laughed as I stood with my mouth open in amazement.

"How did you know about this place?" I asked when I had regained my power of speech. "I never knew it was here.

"My father showed it to me a long time ago," replied Fiona. "We lost a sheep in here once. The stream flows into a big cave and doesn't come out on top of the ground again for ever so far.

"Let's swim," she suggested. "The water in that basin thing's plenty deep enough. It's warm, too." She pulled her dress over her head, flung it on a rock, and scrambled down into the natural pool. She stood knee-deep in the water and laughed up at me. "Come on," she urged. "It's lovely."

I needed no second invitation. Quickly divesting myself of my shorts, I in turn slid and scrambled down the rocks and joined Fiona in the water. We played in the water for a long time, rolling and splashing like two young seals.

Finally, the sun having moved so that the rocks shaded the pool, the water began to feel a little cool, and we decided to get out. The small rocks around the edges of the pool were covered with a bright-green, soft moss that delighted Fiona. "Come and sit on one," she called delightedly. "It feels so soft. Just like a velvet cushion." It did, too.

We climbed out and lay side by side on the grass in a patch of sunlight. The sun dried and warmed our bodies, and we lay and talked drowsily, only half awake.

Finally, the breeze having turned a little chilly with the approach of late afternoon, we reluctantly got up from the grass, put on our clothes, and set off for home.

I don't remember exactly how long I had known Fiona when I first met her mother. It must have been between two and three years. It initiated, nevertheless, one of the unhappiest periods of my life.

Fiona and I were walking homeward early one evening. We had been walking all afternoon. It was autumn, and the moor was blanketed with heather. I had picked several stems of heather and given them to her, and Fiona had twisted them into a garland and made a circlet for her head.

We rounded an outcropping and came into the sunlight. The rays of the evening sun fell full upon Fiona as she stopped momentarily to adjust her heather crown. Her hair moved gently in the breeze. I knew I had never seen anything—or anybody—quite so beautiful.

"Fiona," I said, "did you know that your eyes are exactly the color of the heather?"

She looked at me wonderingly, a little bewildered. Then she smiled. I took a couple of steps toward her—hesitantly. I put my arms around her and kissed her on the lips.

She didn't resist at all. She stood relaxed in my arms for a moment with her lips pressed to mine.

I released her and stood still. I didn't know what to do next. I was afraid to look at her. When I finally summed up sufficient courage to look at her, I was infinitely relieved to see her mouth curved in a faint smile. Her cheeks were flushed, and her eyes were very bright. Neither of us spoke a word. She took my hand, and we walked on.

The following afternoon I approached the place of our usual rendezvous with mixed emotions. Would Fiona be there? I was convinced that I hadn't offended her, yet I couldn't rid myself of a strange premonition of impending disaster.

My steps slowed as the rock where we usually met came into view. I strained my eyes, with a mixture of eagerness and apprehension, to see if she was there. My heart sank. The familiar figure was not seated on the rock, bare brown legs dangling, long hair blowing in the breeze. She was not there.

Someone was there, however—a bigger, unfamiliar figure. I debated whether to turn back and go home or go on. Before I had come to a decision, however, the person seated on the rock, seeing me, rose and walked toward me.

Although I had never seen her before, I recognized Fiona's mother as soon as I could see her face. She had the same wonderful violet eyes as her daughter. She was a rather tall, slender woman. Her face looked kind.

She approached me with a smile, took my hand, and led me back toward the rocks where she had been seated. Her smile and friendly manner reassured me, and my heart beat less wildly.

"You're Arthur, aren't you." It was a statement rather than a question. "Fiona described you exactly. I'm her mother. You no doubt guessed that already."

"Yes, ma'am," I faltered. "She looks a great deal like you. Is something wrong? Is Fiona all right?"

"To be sure she is," her mother assured me. "Don't look so startled. There's nothing wrong."

We sat down together on the big, sun-splashed rock. Fiona's mother drew me closer to her and put her arm gently around my shoulders. "You're right fond of our Fiona," she said. Again, it was more a statement than a question.

"Yes, ma'am," I told her earnestly. "Indeed I am." And, as she continued to look at me thoughtfully, I added, "She's the most beautiful girl I have ever seen."

"She's a bonny little lass," her mother agreed. She broke off, as if reluctant to say what she had planned to say next.

She brushed her hair away from her eyes with a gesture that immediately reminded me of Fiona and put both her hands on my shoulders. "Look at me, Arthur," she demanded. "I'm going to tell you something very important."

I looked at her, and her eyes reflected the fear in my own.

"Yes," she said, half to herself and half to me. "You really think a great deal of my little princess. And she thinks there's nobody like you in all the world."

And suddenly, as if she couldn't bear to say the words: "Do you know who she is?"

"Why, yes, of course," I rejoined, mystified. "She's your daughter."

"She is that," agreed her mother, "and God be thanked for it, but do you know who her father is?"

"Y-yes," I faltered, even more bewildered. "Her father's the shepherd—your—your husband, I mean."

"No, that he's not." She almost spat out the words as if relieved to be rid of them. "Fiona's father and your father are one and the same." And as if to make certain that I could not fail to understand, she reiterated: "Fiona and you have the same father, laddie."

I tried to rise from my seat on the rock. The world seemed to be spinning dizzily.

"Sit you down, laddie," her voice said from what seemed very far away. "And for God's sake, don't look like that. It's not the end of the world."

I don't know how long we sat there together. She did most of the talking. She held me close and talked softly and persuasively.

"So you see, laddie," she summed up, "it'll be best if you and Fiona don't play together anymore. Do you understand what I'm trying to tell you? I know you're awful fond of her, and you want what's best."

"You mean not at all—not ever?" I cried, unbelieving. "You mean I'll never see her again?"

"Oh, you'll see one another again, no doubt. But there'd best be no meetings or walks and that."

"But she'll think I don't—I don't like her anymore," I objected desperately. And hesitantly, "Does she know—what you just told me?"

"No, laddie, she does not. She's always thought the shepherd was her father. I'm going to talk to her tonight. I'm going to tell her what I've just told you. I give you my word. She won't think you've turned against her. I'll tell her that I've forbidden you to see her. She's going to hate me for a spell, but she'll come to understand."

I stood up again. My heart felt as if it had died within me. I could think of nothing to say. Fiona's mother rose also. She looked straight at me, and there were tears in her eyes. "I can see why my little lass took a fancy to you," she said. "You've got your mother's features, but you've the nature of your father."

She bent down and kissed me gently on the forehead, turned, and walked rapidly away.

I don't know how much my father knew of what had taken place. He said nothing to me about it, but several times when I returned from a solitary walk on the moors, I caught his eyes upon me. For several weeks he spent a lot more time with me than usual, taking hours that I knew he could ill spare from his responsibilities so that I would be less alone.

In spite of this, the remainder of that season was, I think, the loneliest period of my life. The expeditions to the moors, previously an eagerly anticipated and eminently satisfying part of my days, ceased to hold any satisfaction for me. It was many months before the healing influence of nature began to weave its spell upon me—her erstwhile ardent devotee. It was a long time before I stopped looking, involuntarily, for a beloved little figure—always heartbreakingly absent—each time I found myself near one or other of our trysting places.

Although we lived only a mile or so from each other, I did not see Fiona again for what must have been almost nine years. As I grew older I had taken over many of my father's responsibilities and cared for a good deal of the overseeing that increasing feebleness now prevented him from doing.

Nevertheless, she was often in my thoughts, and I never took one of my perforce less frequent rambles across the moors without her image crossing my mind. I heard that she had grown into a beautiful young woman, which surprised me not at all. A little later I heard that she had married a young farmer from a neighboring valley, and with all my heart I wished that she might find happiness.

Time went by, and I was surprised one morning to receive a letter addressed in an unfamiliar, feminine handwriting. I was even more surprised to read its contents.

"Dear Arthur," the letter read, "James and I have been blessed with a darling baby boy. He is to be christened next Thursday afternoon at three o'clock. We want you to stand for him and be his godfather. Will you, please? I'd be very happy if you would. Love, Fiona."

I read the short message four or five times before folding it carefully and putting it in my pocket.

It was with some trepidation that, the following Thursday, dressed in my best suit and with my hair carefully brushed, I made my way the short distance to the old Norman church beside the river in the valley below our house. I was early, and no one was there but the Reverend Angus Maconochie, with whom I was only slightly acquainted. He greeted me rather brusquely:

"Good day to ye, young man. Ye'll be the laddie who's to stand godfather to the bairn, I suppose. You're fra the hoose, are ye not? My greetings to the master, your faither. Ye'll no have been a godfather before, I ken, so I'll be just introducin' you to your duties and responsibilities. It's no light matter, ye ken."

The Reverend Maconochie's "instruction," to which I paid, I am afraid, only scant attention, occupied the time until the christening party arrived. Fiona's mother entered the church first, carrying the baby wrapped in a long, white, crocheted shawl. She smiled warmly at me, then leaned over and kissed my cheek. "You're looking fine," she observed. "You're very like him when he was your age."

In spite of the fact that she was almost 10 years older than when I had last seen her, Fiona looked to me not much changed from the child I had known for a brief, idyllic period so long ago. She was tall and rather slender, and her shining, long black hair and remarkable eyes were, I noted, just as beautiful as ever. She whispered something to her husband and came across to where I stood.

"Arthur," she said, with a note of delight in her voice, "I'm so happy you're here. I told James I knew you would. I can't tell you how good it is to see you again." She took my hands in hers, kissed me gravely, and led me across the church to meet her husband.

James Robinson, a tall, rather handsome, pleasant-appearing man, acknowledged the introduction in a friendly manner. I was happy to note that he appeared to be a kindly individual, and it was quite evident that he adored his wife.

The six of us, counting the baby, made our way, led by the minister, Reverend Maconochie, to the stone font at the west end of the church. The lid of the lead-lined container had been removed in readiness, and an inch or two of water had been poured into the basin for the christening.

Fiona took her son from her mother, and the minister proceeded to read the Order of Service for Infant Baptism from the *Book of Common Prayer.* It was a brief ceremony. About halfway through, the minister turned to Fiona. "Hand the child to his godfather," he instructed.

If I had paid proper attention to the good parson's previous instruction, I would probably have been more prepared, but in the circumstances I was taken somewhat by surprise. Smiling at my discomfiture, Fiona placed the baby gently in my arms. I held him awkwardly, unsure whether to grasp him firmly lest he fall or hold him gingerly lest I injure him. I had been the last baby in our house, and my ignorance was complete.

"What name have ye chosen for the bairn?" demanded the Reverend Maconochie.

Fiona looked directly at me as she replied: "We have decided to name our son Arthur."

Tears sprang to my eyes, and, confused, I looked down at the sleeping child.

"Guid, guid," the old minister approved. "A guid name for a laddie. There've been kings in these parts by that name. It's glad I am ye've no chosen one of these outlandish names from a book or from the picture house."

I was anxious to see what my little namesake looked like, but all I could see was the tip of a tiny nose poking out of the shawl and an incredibly small, red fist with the fingers curled tightly together.

I got a better look almost momentarily, though, because the Reverend Maconochie, having dipped his hand into the water in the depths of the font, leaned over and made the sign of the cross on the child's forehead with his wet forefinger. The baby, aroused by the cold water, opened his mouth and emitted a surprisingly loud cry of protest. At the same moment, he opened his eyes, which, I noted with intense satisfaction, were of the same deep blue as his mother's. I held him close to me in a sudden wave of tenderness, which was quickly dissipated by the voice of the Reverend Maconochie.

"Well, let go of the bairn, then," he demanded. "Are ye no going to give him up? Hand the bairn to his mother, and let's be proceedin' with the ceremony."

After the ceremony I had opportunity for only a word with Fiona as we took our leave of each other. Her mother had regained possession of the baby and was anxious to get him home. James Robinson shook my hand and gravely expressed his appreciation before he rejoined his mother-in-law outside the church.

I took Fiona's hand in mine. "Thank you," I whispered.

She kissed me gently on the cheek and rejoined her family.

At the height of the severest cold and snowstorms, my father became quite ill and was forced to take to his bed. Although now very feeble, he still took a lively interest in the affairs of the estate, and it became customary for me to visit him each evening and report to him on the "state of the place" and the doings of the day. I could not help seeing, as I sat and talked with him night after night, that my beloved father was failing fast. He was now an old man, and his physical strength was unequal to his still vital, lively spirit.

One evening, when I entered his room to make my report, I found him quieter than usual. At first he had little to say and, uncharacteristically, no questions to ask. It was as if he had finally relinquished the responsibility of "the place" to me. This realization disturbed me. I knew what his home and his land meant to him. I knew that our family had occupied and cared for this area for more than 200 years, and the thought that my father was now ready to let go and pass on the responsibility to me filled me with apprehension.

For a while we sat silent while the gathering darkness cast shadows around the room. Then my father spoke. "Come closer to me," he requested. "I want to talk with you."

I pulled my chair close to his bedside. I don't know quite what I was expecting. When it came I was greatly surprised and much moved.

"Arthur," he said, struggling up on his pillow so that he could look into my face, "you may find it hard to believe now after all these years, but when she was a young girl, Fiona's mother was every bit as beautiful as Fiona."

I took my father's hand in my own. "No, Father," I assured him, "I don't find it hard to believe at all."

My father was, of course, well known over quite a wide area, and I knew he had many friends. I was, however, unprepared for the number of mourners who were present on the cold April day of his funeral. They filled the tiny church and made a long, straggling line as we made our way behind the casket through the churchyard to his resting place, which had been prepared down beside the river.

I walked with my mother, and I carried a small bouquet of wildflowers that I had picked that morning on the moors behind the house. My mother's face was hidden by her black veil, and she averted her eyes from my unorthodox bouquet.

Arriving at the graveside, I saw Fiona at once. She stood not far from me, close to her mother and her husband. I didn't know whether she had seen me or not. She carried in her hand a small bouquet of wildflowers.

I didn't really hear the minister reading the words of the funeral service as we stood beside the open grave. It didn't really register in my mind when the bearers came forward and lowered the casket into the grave. My mind was not in the churchyard. My mind was out on the moors. I was reliving the times out there on the beautiful, beautiful moorland that I had shared, first with my father, then with Fiona.

The minister's voice had ceased. Some of the people were moving slowly away. I looked up and shivered in the cold wind. A few flakes of snow drifted down and fluttered onto the mass of wreaths that lay beside the grave. A lambing storm, the local people would call it.

I approached the edge of the grave and stood silent, holding my flowers. Suddenly I was conscious that Fiona had left her family and was standing beside me. She looked at me for a moment. Snowflakes drifted whitely onto her black hair. Tears shone on her lashes, and her eyes looked like drowned violets.

We knelt together beside the open grave. Gently she took my little bouquet from my fingers. Twisting the stems of my flowers together with the stems of the flowers she was carrying, she made them into one bouquet and then tenderly placed them on the casket.

I elected to walk home across the moors. The sky was overcast, and occasional snowflakes fluttered down to melt coldly on my face. I began to climb the hill toward the moor and the great gray house vaguely visible in the distance. From the churchyard I caught the notes of the piper, standing by the graveside, his tartan blown by the wind, playing a Highland lament. It must have been the loneliest sound in all the world.

"I'D GIVE 10 YEARS . . ."

"Goodbye then, our Gladys. Be a good girl now, and write reg'lar. Ev'ry Sunday, eh? An' me an' Dad'll see you soon. Soon as 'e gets 'is next leave."

"You'll come down an' see me an' Willy, our mum? Promise. Say you will, our mum. Next week, p'raps? Eh, our mum? Say you will."

Sally looked at the scene around her—looked and listened. She wasn't a talkative child, and the more deeply she felt, the less she said.

The great locomotive straddled the tracks under the glassless roof of St. Pancras Station, puffing out clouds of black smoke with an occasional wisp of white steam, as if impatient to be off. It was a long train, coach after coach right down the Number 3 platform as far as you could see. Every coach carried a sticker on the window with a number—just a number—no names. This was wartime London, and even the evacuees' special—like all the others—was "destination unknown."

There were 2,500 children on this train, their ages ranging from 4 to 15 years. The London "blitz" had just recently been launched, and "Operation Stork" was the current number one priority—to get as many of London's children as possible to comparative safety in the country. They were leaving home—the majority for the first time—"for the duration."

Each child had a small suitcase or haversack with their clothes and a few favorite toys, a package of food for the journey packed by loving hands, and the little square box on their back containing their gas mask. Every child was labeled with a small square of cardboard pinned to coat or sweater in a prominent position and bearing their name, age, school, home address, and next of kin.

Naturally enough, there were some tears. But, for the most part, the excitement of the company of so many others in distress kept the tears at bay. They would come later, and for the present it was better that there should be laughter and shrill voices.

"'It 'im, Joe Brown. 'E says the war won't be done by Christmas. Course it will. My dad's in the Tank Corps. It'll be done long before then. Go on, Joe Brown. 'It 'im with your gas mask."

Three small boys were scuffling on the platform. Sally looked toward them without wholly seeing them and turned her cornflower-blue eyes back to her mother, whose eyes, also blue, were unusually bright. They smiled at one another. Neither of them spoke. They were particularly close, these two—7-year-old Sally and 28-year-old Valerie Mason—closer, perhaps, than most mothers and daughters, and there were many times when words were not necessary.

Henry Jessop paused in his earnest conversation with Grace Colliver and glanced at his watch. Five minutes to go. He'd better blow the whistle and get them all on the train. Jessop was the principal of Peckham Elementary School, and he was in charge of this trip. He was perspiring freely, although the day was cool. He drew his whistle on the silver chain out of his pocket and blew two shrill blasts. *Might as well get it over with,* he thought.

The noise stopped as if cut off at the source. Gladys Jones stopped trying to persuade her mother to make promises that both of them knew she wouldn't be able to keep. The three little boys stopped scuffling around the baggage truck, and a single tear escaped from Valerie Mason's eye and rolled slowly down her cheek. Sally pretended not to notice it.

The score or so of teachers in charge of the children herded them onto the train, assigning them to specific coaches according to the color of the identification cards the children wore. This segregation determined the final destination of each group.

Valerie Mason and her small daughter clung to one another momentarily, and then, released from her mother's arms, Sally joined her group and boarded the train. Neither of them trusted herself to speak. Each was determined not to say "goodbye." It was too irrevocable—too final.

Miss Yeomans—in charge of Sally's group—was far too engrossed with establishing some sort of order out of the inevitable chaos to pay very much attention to one small girl with over-bright blue eyes and a very white face. Sally was never a troublesome child, and Edith Yeomans concerned herself with those whom she was determined to keep an eagle eye on lest they—characteristically—sabotage the whole operation.

"Miss Yeomans, Miss Yeomans, 'Arold 'ere 'as gone an' swiped my tanner. My mum give me sixpence for sweets, an' 'e's took it. 'E's put it in 'is mouth. Make 'im give it back, Teacher."

"'Arold—I mean Harold Simms—return Joseph's tanner—sixpence—at once."

"Miss Yeomans, 'e says 'e's swallered it. Make 'im give it up."

"Really now, you two. I think I'd sooner stay here with the bombs than have to put up with you. Harold, go into the toilet at the end of the corridor and see if you can—er, recover Joseph's sixpence."

"Miss Yeomans, what d'ya take me for, a blinkin' sword swallerer?"

"That'll do, Harold Simms. Do as you're told—immediately."

Within a surprisingly short time, the platform was empty of children, and the guard walked the length of the train, testing every door to make sure all were secure.

The locomotive began to make wheezing, hissing noises indicative of imminent departure, and the host of parents—in the circumstances, quite naturally, mostly mothers—who had drifted together as the children left them, in a sort of common bond of misery, hurried up and down the platform, frantically searching for a beloved small head poking out of one of the carriage windows of the seemingly endless train.

"Stand back now, ladies. You young 'uns, stick your 'eads in," bellowed the guard more as a matter of form than anything else, since he evinced no surprise at the complete lack of response from either group. He blew a short, shrill blast on his whistle, waved his green flag in signal to the engineer, and fell back toward the caboose at the rear of the train.

The mothers surged toward the open windows as the train began to move. Small, waving hands momentarily touched bigger hands as they were carried past each other, and a babel of shrill "goodbyes," "ta-tas," and "cheerios," mingled with some sobbing from the smaller ones, was rapidly drowned out by the noise of the locomotive and the clanking of the wheels on the track as the train pulled out of the station and headed north toward the center of England—the counties of the Midlands.

"All right, everybody, inside the compartment and sitting down," called out Miss Yeomans. "I want all those windows closed before I count to 10."

I first saw the light of day in late October 1923 in this house on the edge of the Derbyshire moors. A blizzard was raging.

My sister, Mary, was with me on a visit to an old farmhouse as we wandered the moors. The farm children brought out toys, and their mother snapped this picture.

This "portrait" picture was taken just before I left for boarding school at 9 years old.

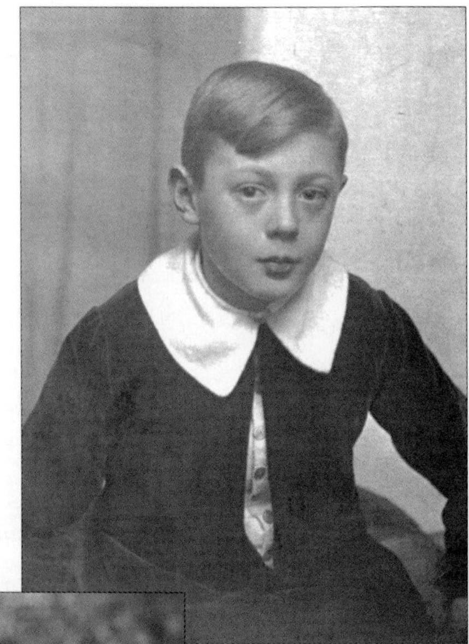

This is my graduation picture from Newbold College, where I had been pursuing a Master of Arts degree in English.

I am standing behind a group of my students at the school for missionaries' children in Nairobi, East Africa. Sheila is on the far left in the front row.

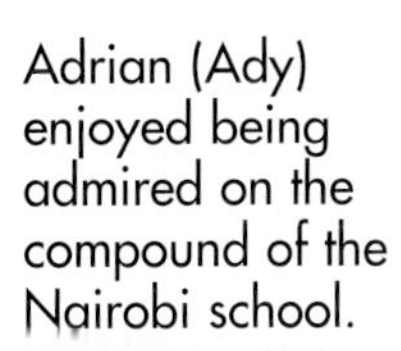

Adrian (Ady) enjoyed being admired on the compound of the Nairobi school.

Ady and his daddy are ready for Sabbath school in Nairobi.

This picture of Ady was taken just before his diagnosis with "childhood leukemia."

My family and I wait at the Nairobi airport for the flight to London to seek treatment for Ady's recently diagnosed leukemia.

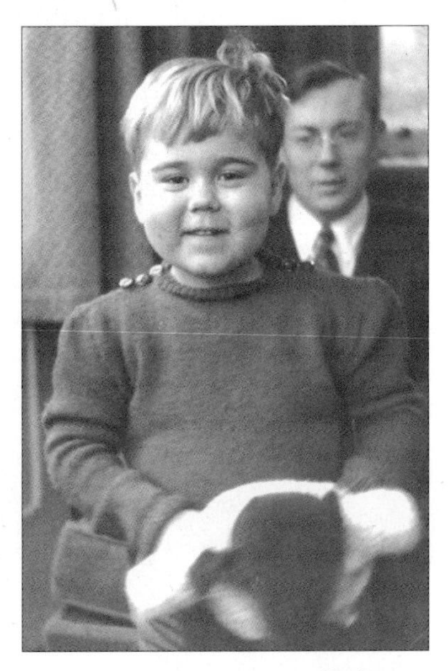

I am with Ady and a stuffed companion during one of Ady's several periods of chemotherapy.

Ady pauses in Trafalgar Square in London on the way to the hospital for a further session of chemotherapy.

Ady, third from the front, plays in the park with other children of the "terminal ward" in London, England. Staff Nurse Kirby took the children to the park on her weekly "day off."

Beloved Nurse Kirby plays with Ady on the veranda of the "terminal ward" at The Hospital for Sick Children in London.

Ady stands with me and one of his favorite toys.

Ady poses with his adored baby sister. He was very protective of baby "Noni."

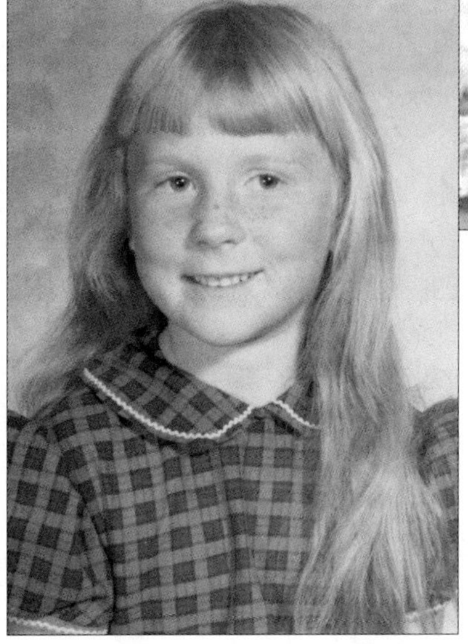

This is Victoria Jane (Vicki), my youngest daughter, at about 7 years old.

I stand with my daugther, Veronica Anne (Noni), at her wedding; she married David Lawrence Crockett, who currently pastors the Yakima, Washington, Seventh-day Adventist Church.

Here is Veronica and her family, left to right: her husband, Dave; Allison; Ben; Jessica; Abe; and Veronica.

Here is Vicki and her family, left to right: Amanda; Vicki's husband, Marvin; Vicki; and Ian.

"Do stop it, our Emily. I'm coming back in. Just 'cause you're a year older than me don't put you in charge, y'know. Now look what you've done, grabbing onto me like that. You've ripped my best drawers. Brand-new they was, too. I'd make you give me a pair o' yours if you didn't 'ave such a big, fat—"

"That'll do, Ivy. Both of you come into the carriage and sit down.

"If I get to the end of this journey alive and rational, the rest of the war will seem like a picnic," Edith Yeomans told herself. Nevertheless, she felt genuine compassion for her young charges—"rough diamonds" though some of them were. For many of them this was their first train ride, and the countryside would be like a different world to them after a lifetime—even a short lifetime—spent in London's crowded, grimy East End.

Valerie Mason's last glimpse of Sally as the train pulled out was of a slender, terribly vulnerable little figure pressed against the carriage door. Her jaunty little red beret was pushed askew on her long, flaxen hair by the press of those crowding around her. Her lips were pressed tightly together, and as she passed by her mother on the platform, she essayed a wavering smile.

Valerie's heart turned over in her chest. It was just like this she had looked (was it only three months ago?) when the telegram had arrived.

Valerie had just reached home from the early shift at the aircraft plant and Sally had been back from school only a few minutes when the *rat-tat* came at the door. Valerie, glancing through the window, had seen the telegraph boy's red bicycle by the sidewalk and, her heart sinking, had tried to call the child back. But Sally had excitedly run to open the door.

"Mum, there's a boy here with a telegram—from the War Office. He wants to know if he should wait for a reply."

With trembling fingers, Valerie had taken the buff-colored envelope—"On His Majesty's Service"—from her small daughter's hand. She had opened it—although there was no need. She already knew exactly what it would say: "His Majesty's Government regrets to inform you that your husband, Sergeant William Mason, of the Royal Kent Regiment, was killed in action in France on January 23, 1940."

She had leaned against the doorpost until the world stopped spinning around. Somehow she had managed to steady her voice sufficiently to tell the waiting boy: "No thank you. There will be no reply."

She had closed the door slowly and turned to face the waiting child—quiet now, and pale with mounting apprehension. "Oh, God," she had said silently, "I would give 10 years of my life not to have to tell her . . ."

Valerie bit her lips and choked back the tears that she felt perilously near the surface. What would people think of her—walking down the streets crying like a baby? She nearly ran down the platform and left the station, turning in the direction of her home almost by instinct, as she could barely see where she was going. Just as she turned the corner of her street, the air-raid warning sounded, but she scarcely heard it. She must get home. She must tell Rose that Sally had got off all right. It always helped to talk to Rose.

When she arrived at the entryway she shared with Rose—her neighbor and best friend—Rose was waiting outside for her. Being Rose, she took charge at once.

"There you are. I was 'opin' you'd get 'ome before the sirens went. It's just about 'is time, y'know. 'E always seems to 'it it about teatime, don't 'e? Proper nasty, I call it. Never mind. Let's not bother our 'eads about 'im. Come inside by the fire. I've got the kettle on, and the crumpets'll toast up in a jiffy."

Rose shrugged the Luftwaffe off her ample shoulders with characteristic equanimity. Her philosophy was "If you're going to get it, you'll get it, so why worry?" She had been "bombed-out" twice, but she was neither nervous nor really resentful. The thing that caused Rose most concern was the meagerness of the monthly tea ration ("about what you could put in your eye"), although she had "contacts" from whom she could "organize" a bit extra now and then.

Rose had been a tower of strength ever since Bill had been killed. Rose didn't miss anything that went on in the neighborhood. She had seen the telegraph boy. Beneath an undeniably large and—to some—forbidding exterior, Rose harbored a correspondingly large and compassionate heart. She hadn't given Valerie a chance to really get down to crying. She had waited until she thought Valerie had had time to break the news to Sally and then had put in an appearance. Contrary to her usual practice—for she was neither inquisitive nor interfering—she had knocked on the door and entered without waiting for an invitation.

She had apparently ignored the two figures clasped in each other's arms in the big rocker by the fire. "There's no need to say nothin'," she had announced. "If I was to say anythin', it wouldn't be fit for young ears. The tea's made, and you'd best 'urry on over before it gets cold."

Valerie remembered that as the strongest cup of tea she'd tasted in months. She learned later that Rose had used up all of her own tea ration and had begged some off the neighbors on either side. Rose wouldn't dream of asking anybody for anything for herself, but she wasn't averse to begging for somebody else—after she'd given all she had.

They had stayed at Rose's house all that night. Her man was away with the Royal Kents too, and Rose had declared, when the air-raid sirens sounded as usual soon after nightfall, that she felt "sort o' nervy-like tonight somehow, and can't abide staying by myself." The idea of Rose being "nervy" was a little like the Rock of Gibraltar looking shaky, but as Rose herself had observed on sundry appropriate occasions: "The truth's the truth, and a lie's a lie, depending on what you mean by it," and they had stayed the night—"to keep Rose company."

Now again, in this new "bereavement," Valerie quite naturally turned to Rose for strength and comfort. They sat on the hearth rug together, toasting crumpets by the fire, and Valerie described the departure of the evacuees for Rose, and, for the first time since she had been notified of his death, she spoke of her husband—big, blond, handsome Bill Mason. Bill and Valerie had been deeply in love with each other ever since they had first met nine years earlier, and they had both worshipped little Sally with an adoration that she had wholeheartedly reciprocated.

After the initial storm of grief, Sally had rarely spoken of her father. Like Valerie, young though she was, her feelings sometimes seemed to be too deep for expression in words. Once or twice, however, Valerie had come upon the little girl alone in her bedroom holding tightly to the picture of her father in his uniform—which normally had pride of place on her dresser—either trying hard to control her sobbing or else gazing dry-eyed at the picture with such a stricken look on her small face that Valerie's heart missed a beat. At these times mother and daughter would fly into each other's arms and, often without words, find comfort in a shared grief and a passionate affection.

On the evening of "evacuation day," after she left Rose and returned to her house, Valerie kept busy "tidying up" and preparing for the next day's work. She managed, somewhat to her surprise, to remain dry-eyed until—from sheer force of habit—she turned on the radio to listen to *Children's Hour.* "Though what the neighbors will think, I can't imagine," she said to herself. "Me sitting here listening to Andy Pandy and Bill and Ben, the Flowerpot Men." Somehow it made her feel a little closer to Sally, listening to the children's stories that the little girl had always delighted in.

It was the change in the familiar ritual, however, that pierced her control and started the hot tears flowing. Inspired, doubtless, by the events of the day, the *Children's Hour* "uncle," when it came to sign-off time, made a not inappropriate addition to the usual "Good night, children."

"Good night, children," he said. "Good night, children—everywhere."

And Valerie Mason—rather like the bigger, older version of Sally that, in effect, she was—seized her husband's picture from its place of honor on the mantelpiece and sobbed as if her heart would break.

Somewhat to her surprise, Edith Yeomans did survive the ordeal of delivering 75 youngsters in varying degrees of excitement, ranging from mild stimulation to near hysteria—to the Village Hall in Sudbury, the tiny North Derbyshire village that was to be their home "for the duration."

Considering that it was a "first ever" situation, the placing of the children in homes, or "billets," in the village went surprisingly smoothly. The ladies of the local Women's Voluntary Services had everything well organized and had compiled, ahead of time, a roster of the homes available, classified according to the number of children who could be accommodated and the sex and age preferences.

There were, inevitably, some annoyances and frustrations, though not really sufficient in quantity or degree to warrant Edith Yeomans' description of the scene as the "slave market." But it had been a very exhausting day, and Miss Yeomans was tired. She slumped wearily onto a chair in a corner of the hall and watched the eager, efficient WVS ladies take over.

"Righto, Mrs. Sims, I know you said a little girl, and a little girl you shall have. About 8 years old, you said? Brown hair and hazel eyes so she looks like your husband. Mrs. Sims, you are providing a temporary home for the duration of the war—you are not adopting the child. Yes, if such a child is available, you shall have her."

"Mrs. Reynolds, you said you could manage two boys, didn't you? You don't care how big or how small or what color hair. Just so they need a home and a bit of loving. Bless you, Mrs. Reynolds. I've got just the pair for you: two brothers . . ."

Cruelly, perhaps, but quite naturally, the most attractive and best-cared-for children were placed first. Pounced on by eager foster parents, they were registered and whisked off to their new homes in short order.

Sally, very bewildered but undeniably appealing in her short, print dress, white socks, and scarlet coat and beret, almost immediately took the eye of Mrs. Parry, a rather stout woman well past middle age, whose own family was long since grown and dispersed in various directions. She and her husband were tenant farmers on my father's estate.

Not only motherly but also perceptive, Mrs. Parry noted the child's somewhat retiring manner and sensed the underlying sadness behind the blue eyes.

"'Allo, ducks, what's your name? 'Ave you ever been to a farm—with 'orses an' sheep an' cows, now?"

"Oh, no, ma'am. I've always lived in London with my mum and—with my mum," replied Sally. She rather liked the look of this big woman. She seemed as if she would be very kind and somehow understanding. In a way, she reminded her of Rose. She was different from Rose, yet somehow the same.

"Would you like to come an' stay with me an' Mr. Parry, dear? Just for a while, y' know. Till all that 'ere's done with. We'd both love to 'ave you if you would."

The small girl and the big woman appraised one another—and both liked what they saw.

Mrs. Parry threw in the clincher: "Your mum could come up an' see you, y' know, any time she can get off. She can come an' stay as long as she wanted, an' you could show 'er around like."

Mrs. Parry's eyes moistened as Sally flashed her a shy, fleeting smile.

"Yes, please, ma'am. I think I'd like that—if you wouldn't mind having me. I'd try not to get in the way. I don't know anything about cows or horses, but I can wash dishes, and I make my own bed."

"Bless you, luv, you won't be in the way. Me an' Mr. Parry'll just love 'avin' you. I know we'll all get along champion. That's settled then. Come on; let's go an' tell Mrs. Green at the table as we've chose each other."

Mrs. Parry took the small hand in her big one and felt the tiny fingers quiver slightly as the two of them threaded their way through the knots of women and children and out into the sunlit street.

"I'll tell you what we'll do," she said. "The very first thing, we'll go an' buy a picture postcard an' then go to the post office an' you can write on it an' tell your mum your address so she knows where you are an' can write to you, see. You can send her a proper letter after we get 'ome an' get settled a bit. Then we'll go an' meet Mr. Parry. 'E's down at the cattle market doin' a bit o' business. 'E's got the car down there somewhere."

Mr. Parry was a tall man, about the same age as his wife, but not nearly so heavy. He had graying hair, bushy eyebrows, and kindly, twinkling eyes. Sally took to him on sight.

"I knew as I could trust the missis to pick the best," he told Sally on the way to the farm in the car. "After all, she picked me, didn't she?"

Sally felt at home at once in the big, rambling farmhouse. She liked the bright, warm kitchen, where the table was all set for tea. Everything was bright and shining, from the black fireplace and bread oven, where a coal fire was burning brightly, to the copper warming pan hanging on the wall beside the grandfather clock.

Tom, the old black cat, got up lazily from his sleeping place in the armchair and came over to inspect the small newcomer. He pushed his velvety nose into Sally's hand and purred loudly when she gently scratched his head.

"There you are. Tom likes you," announced Mr. Parry triumphantly. "I told you. We've all got good taste in this family."

After a quick wash and a meal that gave no indication of food rationing, Sally sat back from the table, wiped the crumbs from her mouth, and began to take stock of her surroundings. She felt suddenly tired.

Mrs. Parry, with the watchful eye of long experience, recognized that the little girl had had about all the new experiences she could absorb for one day.

"Well now, how about an early night tonight?" she suggested. "Tomorrow Mr. Parry'll show you around the place. There's ducks an' chickens an' lambs an' calves. You're goin' to like it 'ere."

She led the way upstairs and opened the door to a small room with a dormer window looking out onto a meadow. In the distance Sally could see the setting sun glinting on the water of a duck pond.

The room was furnished cheerfully and simply with child-size furniture. The covers on the bed and the cushions on the small rocker were made of a bright, flowered, chintz material. On the wall was a picture of a chubby, small girl with long, flaxen braids.

"This used to be Thelma's room," Mrs. Parry explained. "She's my youngest. She's 19 now. In the WAC (Women's Army Corps) in North Africa.

"Do you want me to 'elp you unpack?" she inquired. "Or would you sooner do it yourself? There's plenty of room in the dresser for your things, an' you can 'ang your coat and dresses in the wardrobe."

After Sally was bathed and in her nightgown, Mrs. Parry came in to brush her hair. Her quick eye took in the arrangement the child had made of her small possessions: her brush and comb and hand mirror on the dresser, and the two pictures that the little girl had placed together on a chair close to her bed—one of a smiling, blond woman, unmistakably Sally's mother, and the other of a handsome man in military uniform.

"I know just exactly what you need," she told the child, brushing the long, shining blond hair with firm, sure strokes. "And just as soon as I'm done with your 'air, I'll go an' get it."

The brushing finished, she tucked Sally into bed and left the room. She returned almost immediately with a small, low bedside table that she placed beside the head of Sally's bed.

"There y'are, luv," she announced. "There's something for you to put your things on. I'll leave the door a bit open now, an' if you want something, or if you want to talk or anything, you just call me. Our room's just across the way, an' we'll be sure to hear you. Don't be frightened if old Tom comes in to see you toward mornin'. He's taken a fancy to you an' might just want to come in an' keep you company."

She kissed the little girl—half asleep now—and returned downstairs to where her husband anxiously awaited her in the big kitchen.

"Is she all right?" he demanded. "Do you think she's goin' to like us?"

Mrs. Parry smiled at him indulgently. "For an old man, you're a regular fussbudget," she chided. "O' course she's all right. She's tired out, o' course—an' strange, too, at first. But she'll settle down. I think perhaps 'er father's dead—in the war, y'know. She didn't say—but I think that's about the size of it."

"Pretty little lass, isn't she?" observed Jim Parry, reaching for a glowing ember from the fireplace to relight his pipe. "Puts me in mind of our Thelma in a way, when she was little. Thinner, of course, an' paler, but fair like 'er."

"Oh, we'll soon take care o' that," promised Mrs. Parry. "A week or two o' fresh air an' sunshine and plenty o' good country food'll soon put some color into 'er cheeks an' some flesh on 'er bones." She glanced across at her husband, sucking on his pipe and looking into the fire, and smiled again. "An' stop worryin' an' come to bed, you great silly. She'll like you. I never yet knew a young 'un as didn't."

Not naturally an adaptable child, Sally fell into the ways of the household remarkably quickly. As his wife had prophesied, she took to Jim Parry immediately, and before long the two were inseparable. She attended the village school in the mornings along with the other evacuees, the afternoon session being reserved for the village children, as the schoolroom was not big enough to accommodate both groups at the same time. But in the afternoons she followed "Grandpa Parry," as she learned to call him, around like a small shadow as he went about his work around the farm, and it was hard to say which of the pair was the most delighted with the arrangement.

Mrs. Parry chuckled contentedly to herself as she spied them through the kitchen window, the little girl clinging to his hand and talking animatedly as they crossed the yard on their way from the barn after afternoon milking. Occasionally she would indulge in a little affectionate teasing of her husband as they got ready for bed after a busy day.

"You're looking 10 years younger, I do declare," she told him, "since you started goin' 'round with that young blond. Put a new lease o' life into you, she 'as."

Half embarrassed, but secretly pleased, Jim Parry gave his wife a good-natured poke in the ribs. "Oh aye," he admitted. "I've sort o' got used to 'avin' 'er around. Can't remember what it was like before she came. Anyway, you seem to be pretty good friends with 'er yourself."

"I think we got the sweetest little lass of the whole bunch," Mrs. Parry declared. "I've got so as I can 'ardly believe she's not really ours."

"Dear Mummy," the letter began. "I've got so much to tell you I don't know where to start. Grandpa and Grandma Parry are real nice. So's Tom. He's our cat. And there's four horses and two dogs and lots of cows an' a real live donkey just like the one at Briten Sands last year. Remember, Mum? An' Grandpa Parry says I can ride him, p'raps tomorrow. . . .

"Oh, Mummy, I do miss you so. It's not so bad in the daytime cause there's so much to do, but when I go to bed I just wish and wish you could come and kiss me good night. I'm trying to be brave—like you said—but sometimes, after Grandma Parry has gone downstairs, I can't help crying just a bit. Can you come and see me soon? You'll love it here. Please come. . . ."

April turned to May, and the days grew longer and warmer. Just as Ruth Parry had predicted, Sally grew rosier and plumper. With the advent of the really warm days of late May, she experienced the freedom of running around in the meadows wearing only her brief panties. She enjoyed running barefoot through the cool grass and feeling the unaccustomed caress of the sun's rays on her bare skin. Sometimes, when it was particularly warm, she was even permitted to "paddle" in the shallow creek that flowed through the lower pasture and fish for minnows—"tiddlers," Grandpa Parry called them—with a fine-meshed net and an empty jam jar.

After one such occasion, she returned triumphantly to the house with her "catch" to display no less than six minnows and three sticklebacks.

"My, you're getting to be quite a fisherman," agreed Ruth Parry admiringly. "An' won't your ma be surprised when she comes to see you next month? Why, you're as brown as a berry, an' you've grown a full inch, I declare. Hasn't she, Jim?" She appealed to her husband, who had just come into the kitchen, for corroboration.

"She 'as that," he averred. "An' she gets prettier every day."

Sally blushed with pleasure, put her jar of fish in a shady spot on the windowsill, and went off upstairs to change her wet clothes for supper.

The days followed one another in rapid succession as the spring turned into the "best summer we've 'ad since I can remember," Mrs. Parry declared. School let out for the summer, and Sally spent all of her time running around the meadows and farm buildings, paddling in the creek, and "helping" Grandpa Parry in the hayfield, riding beside him on the horse-rake as he raked the drying grass into long windrows preparatory to gathering it into "haycocks" and eventual stacking them in the barn. Tractor fuel—being imported—was scarce. Much of the fuel that began its long journey from the Persian Gulf to Britain ended up at the bottom of the Atlantic. The German blockade of England was tightening, and the U-boats were sinking an alarmingly high percentage of the ships that attempted to run the blockade with cargoes of food and fuel for the beleaguered island.

But as far as Sally was concerned, there was only one thing wrong with the idyllic existence she was enjoying—the separation from her mother. That . . . and Crumple. Crumple was one of the Parry's dairy cows, and she was the only member of the ménage that Sally didn't adore wholeheartedly. Sally loathed and feared Crumple—ever since the day the uncertain-tempered creature had chased her clear across the pasture one evening as she was helping Grandpa Parry drive the herd in for milking. Sally had never known she could run so fast, and she vowed, as, breathless and pale, she reached the fence only a couple of yards ahead of the snorting, bellowing animal, that she would never go near a horrid cow again.

But a moment or two in the comforting arms of Grandpa Parry soon calmed her down. Evening milking was delayed for 10 or 15 minutes as Jim Parry held the little quivering figure tightly, wiping away the tears—tears partly of anger and partly of fear—and kissed her gently on the top of her shining head. By the time he was ready to give his attention to the impatient, bellowing herd, Jim Parry had Sally half convinced that old Crumple didn't really mean any harm: "It's just that she's got a bit of the devil in 'er an' likes to chase anybody as'll run from 'er. She wouldn't really 'urt you. She's been sort o' crotchety ever since she banged up 'er 'orn when she was young. That's 'ow she got 'er name, y'know. An' she's about the best milker in the 'erd."

So holding tightly to Grandpa Parry's hand, a tearstained and somewhat flushed Sally went around to where old Crumple was secured, and told her that she would forgive her this time, but that she must never, never do it again.

Sally still had reservations about Crumple, though—reservations she expressed privately in her letter to her mother that weekend:

"Dear Mummy," she wrote, "the most terrifyin' thing happened to me yesterday. Crumple chased me. She didn't catch me, though, She's a fat old cow in our herd. I didn't half run fast. Grandpa Parry says I should train for the Olympics. In some ways this is a perfectly dangerous place. Don't worry about me, though. I'm fine. Oh, Mummy, I can hardly believe it's only a week more till I see you. I haven't seen you for years, seems like. What do you look like? I mean, have you changed a lot? I love you lots and lots. I hope you haven't changed much cause I think you're just beautiful. Your loving daughter, Sally Mason. PS: Grandma Parry says I'm as brown as a berry. What's a berry?"

During the next day or two, Sally could scarcely keep still for excitement over her mother's forthcoming visit. She talked of it constantly, and when human ears were temporarily unavailable, she would tell any of the animals within hearing that her mother was coming—soon.

Perhaps because he was the first to welcome her when she arrived at the farm, old Tom, the farm cat, was Sally's favorite among all the varied animals she had learned to love. And it was Tom she was playing with in her room when the telegram came.

Mr. Parry was washing up for supper in the kitchen, and Sally was lying on her back on her bed with her legs in the air, telling the cat—who was seated on her chest, purring contentedly—for the fiftieth time about the forthcoming visit.

The boy on the red bicycle rode in through the yard gate, parked his bike under the kitchen window, and rapped on the door.

Ruth Parry looked up with sudden apprehension from the table she was setting and hurried to the door. Her face white, she tore open the envelope and read the message on the form.

Her lips trembling, she managed to turn back toward her husband, who was drying his face on the roller towel that hung behind the door. "Give the lad a shillin', Jim," she said in a strained voice that caused her husband to look at her sharply. "Tell 'im there's no reply."

"Steady on, old girl," admonished Jim Parry, putting his big arm around his wife's shaking shoulder as he dismissed the telegraph boy. "What's up, eh? Is it Thelma?"

Ruth Parry, unable to reply, thrust the telegram into her husband's still wet hand.

"Parry, Sudbury, Derbyshire," he read. "Valerie Mason killed last night in heavy raid STOP I'll be down to see Sally tomorrow STOP." It was signed "Aunt Rose."

I'LL HOLD YOU WHILE IT HURTS

Big Jim Parry, suddenly looking like an old man, guided his wife to a chair. From upstairs came the sound of a child's voice singing softly: "Pussy cat, pussy cat, where have you been? I've been up to London to visit the queen."

Jim and Ruth Parry looked at each other, noting the tears on each other's face. Jim was the first to speak. "There now, lass," he said, his voice breaking in a desperate attempt to comfort, "sit you there a bit. I'd best go on up an' tell her . . ."

Ruth Parry wiped her eyes on her apron and stood up.

"Thank you, Jim," she said, avoiding his eyes, "but I must tell 'er myself. I'm kind of like a mother to 'er in a way, an' I must do it. Sit you 'ere—an' pray for us both. I'd give 10 years of my life not to 'ave to go up them stairs."

She took the telegram from her husband's hand and started toward the stairs.

"Sally," she called in a voice quite unlike her own, "I've got a—letter—'ere from a neighbor of yours in London. Calls 'erself your Aunt Rose . . ."

YOU HAVE TO LET IT GO

She was 7 years old, a year younger than I, and she had short, brown hair and dark-blue eyes. She was tall for her age, with suntanned arms and legs.

Jocelyn was not remotely like the rest of her family, either in appearance or temperament. Her mother, Lucy Potter, was big, blond, and outgoing. Lucy's other daughter, Margie, 5 years old, was a tiny replica of her mother.

Neither child ever knew her father. Remarkably, his identity in the small, close-knit English village was known only to Lucy and the respective fathers. They were never mentioned. They were just not part of the picture.

Jocelyn, unlike her talkative, bubbly sibling, spoke little. She went about in a dream, lost, it seemed, in a world of her own. These days she might have been diagnosed as autistic, but she was not. Her withdrawal from consciousness was selective and far from complete. In the village she was characterized as "a quiet child."

I met her, quite fortuitously, early one spring morning immediately after I had found a bird's nest on the edge of the moor, where I was prospecting around, deciding how to spend my day. She was engaged in her daily chore of delivering cans of milk from a farm to several of the neighbors' cottages, a task that helped, marginally, to augment her family's income. She had delivered her milk and was returning with the empties when I saw her some distance away.

I could not resist telling someone about my marvelous discovery. I knew of her, but had never actually made her acquaintance.

"Jocelyn," I called. "Jocelyn Potter. Come and look." I beckoned vigorously.

She hesitated, considered for a moment, then came over and joined me. "What do you want?" she asked in her high, clear voice. "What do you want me for?"

"Look," I said triumphantly, pointing to the nest. "Just look."

We bent over the nest, our heads together, lost in awe at the incredible beauty of the three speckled eggs. We admired their wonderful shape and color for several minutes, then straightened up and looked at each other.

"Meadow pipit's eggs," she decided, taking my hand. "Come on. The hen will want to come back," she explained, as if to an infant. "Let's leave her alone. You won't take them now, will you?" she demanded.

"Of course not," I replied indignantly. "I never take birds' eggs. I just wanted to look at them. Aren't they beautiful?"

"Well, boys do, you know," she said, looking at me sternly. Then she softened: "Thank you for showing them to me."

She gathered up her milk cans from the grass where she had laid them. "I have to take these cans back to the farm," she told me. "You can come with me if you want to."

A carefully brought-up young person, well aware that a gentleman always carries a lady's burdens, I took the cans from her. She relinquished them graciously, recognizing her place in the order of things.

After we had deposited the milk cans in the farm dairy, I offered to escort her home. Interpreting her silence as acquiescence, I continued to accompany her toward the village.

I sneaked an occasional glance to see what she looked like. I knew she was aware of my observation, but she made no response, feigning oblivion to my inspection.

Although younger, she was almost as tall as I was, and she wore a short, blue dress that, I concluded, would have been a better fit when she was two years younger. It was made even shorter because, evidently in a burst of creativity, Jocelyn had torn a strip from the hem to contrive a "ribbon" for her hair. She was barefoot and, except for the aforementioned "ribbon," bareheaded. I decided the overall effect, though somewhat bizarre, was pleasing.

The following morning, and many subsequent mornings, Jocelyn was there as I, released from the nursery, was embarking on my early expeditions to the moors. She would, I knew, have denied that she was waiting for me, but, I noted, she always came the same way and wasn't hurrying.

Over the weeks and months we established a satisfying, if not exciting, relationship. Jocelyn was as enchanted with natural things as I was, and we often had delightful "finds" to share with each other.

We didn't talk a great deal. I was by no means a loquacious child, and Jocelyn had the rare gift of not speaking unless she had something to say.

On only one occasion I saw my quiet little friend in what could be called an excited frame of mind. She carried only one milk can, which she held very carefully in both hands.

"What have you got there, Jocelyn?" I demanded. "Where is the rest of the milk?"

"Shh!" she admonished. "Don't make a noise. Just look."

She very carefully removed the lid from the can and held it out to me. Clinging to the side of the can was one of the most beautiful creatures I had ever seen. A huge moth, bigger than any I had seen before, slowly made its way toward the neck of the can and daylight. Its wings, which opened and closed slowly as it climbed, were marked with stripes and spots in the most beautiful shades of blue and brown and green and gold. Its antennae were edged in what looked to us like tiny feathers. Its body was thick and heavy-looking, and its legs looked incredibly fragile for such a large creature.

I gasped. "Oh, Jos," I exclaimed. "It's beautiful! It's huge! What is it? Where did you find it?"

"It's a moth," responded Jocelyn, a bit scornfully. "I don't know what kind. I found it in the dairy when I went in to get the milk."

"Oh, Jos," I said again. "It's wonderful. What are you going to do with it?"

"After I've delivered the milk, I'm going to put it in the barn," declared Jocelyn. "You've got to help me. You can watch to see that nobody sees me while I let it go."

"Oh, Jos," I repeated in what was becoming a sort of refrain, "how can you bear to let it go? It's so beautiful."

Jocelyn fixed her big, dark eyes on me and spoke earnestly: "Don't you see? I have to let it go so it will stay beautiful. If I try to keep it, it will die and shrivel up and be all ugly. Don't you see?" she almost pleaded.

After one last, lingering moment of admiration, we accomplished our mission, releasing the moth in the big barn behind the dairy and returning undetected to the cache of milk cans.

Jocelyn rinsed out the moth's milk can with a little milk she had saved for the purpose of removing all traces of its temporary tenant. Then she wiped out the can with the hem of her dress and replaced it with the others.

We spoke even less than usual on our way home, but somewhere along the way, Jocelyn felt for my hand.

When we reached the place, out of sight of her home, where, upon Jocelyn's insistence, we always parted, she released my hand and smiled at me. "I'm glad you got to see it too," she said.

This happened a couple of years before I went away to school and we saw each other less often and, eventually, not at all.

Several years later, after the war, I went back to the village with a vague idea of looking up Jocelyn, or at least finding out what had happened to her. The first family member I located was Margie, still blond, still very pretty, still friendly and outgoing, and vociferously happy to see me. She was a lot like her mother must have been at her age. She was also married (I think) and had three small children.

"Jos," she said finally, when we were done exclaiming over each other and patting each other to see if we were real, "poor Jos. She always liked you, you know. A strange one, our Jos."

I decided to interpret this as a compliment of sorts.

"No, she never married. Probably seen enough of 'married' life around home." She chuckled. "It wasn't all bad, though, you know. We had our good times."

"But, Margie, where is she now?" I demanded. "What happened to her?"

"Oh, she was a nurse, you know," said Margie, just as if I had been privy to the entire village's wartime experiences. "She went over to Normandy after D-day to help set up a field hospital. She never came back."

Mother Lucy, it turned out, had moved into town early in the war to do war work. "Hah, war work," sneered some of the spiteful ones I happened to speak with. "You can guess the kind of war work Lucy Potter was doin'."

I located the address Margie had given me, and found Lucy at home. She was scrubbing the front doorstep and at first failed to recognize me, regarding me with some suspicion. After I made myself known to her, however, she greeted me warmly, giving me a spontaneous and generous hug.

"Well, now," she said, "fancy seeing you. How did you find me, then?" she inquired. "Have you been back to the old village? Changed, ain't it? Did you see our Margie?"

"Yes," I replied. "Yes to everything. I went to the village. Yes, it has changed, and yes, I saw Margie. She's as pretty as ever, and just as friendly, and she has three beautiful children."

"Yes, indeed," Lucy agreed. "Takes after her ma, Margie does."

We sat side by side on the step. We avoided looking at each other, each of us well aware of what must come next.

The more courageous of us two, Lucy spoke first: "You heard about poor Jos, then?" she said. "I expect our Margie told you." Her eyes overflowed, and she reached out her arms to me.

We held each other for several minutes, moistening each other's clothing.

"There now," she said at last, sitting upright, dabbing her eyes, and tentatively patting at the damp patch on my shirt. "Look what we've done to each other. What will folks think, us sitting here like this? Come inside, then, and I'll make a pot of tea.

"You know," she confided as we sat in the immaculately clean kitchen drinking our tea, "folks thought as I didn't care about my kids, things being the way they were. But I loved those kids. I loved all of 'em. I did the best I could."

"Mrs. Potter," I began, but she put her hand on my knee and stopped me.

"Enough of the Mrs. Potter," she directed. "I know you always called me that, and I appreciated it, but why don't you call me Lucy?"

I began again: "Lucy," I said earnestly, "I know you loved those children. I've always known that. They knew it too, and they loved you. Margie said as much just now. 'We had some good times, you know,' she told me."

"Did she now?" mused Lucy, a lot brighter. "Thank you for telling me. That means a lot to me."

"Lucy," I said as I stood up to leave some time later, "you don't have any pictures of Jos around, do you by any chance?"

"Bless you, I don't," she told me. "You know I was bombed out when they came after Royces [the Rolls-Royce factory] that time, and I lost every blessed thing. I'm sorry. I'd have been happy to have given you one if I had any. I did have a few, but we weren't a lot for picture takin' in them days."

She took both my hands in hers. "I'm goin' to give you a kiss," she said, and with a flash of old fire, "You can tell them old witches in the village if you go back that you've been kissin' Lucy Potter. That'll give 'em something to gossip about."

Her expression softened. "You were right fond of Jos when you were kiddies," she said. It was a statement rather than a question. "And neither hell nor high water could stop her from heading out with them milk cans on the dot of seven o'clock. And it wasn't because she was addicted to deliver milk, either.

"I'm glad you came," she said, releasing my hands. "I'm sorry about the picture. I suppose all we've got now is the pictures in our heads."

I never saw Lucy or Margie again. I went back to town, to college, to the altar, and eventually to the other side of the Atlantic Ocean. And that, except for the pictures in our heads, is the end of the story.

"PILOT ME"

As a young boy, I had had peripheral contact with Seventh-day Adventists and the Adventist church, having an elderly aunt who became involved with Seventh-day Adventists in her peripatetic meanderings around the world. However, I was neither, as yet, involved nor committed.

My aunt Mary, nevertheless, had persuaded our parents to permit her to enroll my teenage sister in Newbold College, the Adventist college at that time operating on a country estate in the county of Warwickshire, England.

Emotionally close to my only sibling, I persuaded a friend of the family to take me to Newbold Revel, the tiny village where the school was located in an erstwhile mansion in rural surroundings.

We arrived early on a Friday evening. It was a beautiful, mild, autumn evening. The sun was just setting, so we asked the taxi (cab) driver to drop us off at the beginning of the long, winding driveway that led to the school.

It was very quiet and still—silent, except for the occasional cry of a night bird alerted by our passing and a rustling in the undergrowth signaling that, despite appearances, we were not quite alone.

Then, after a few minutes, as we approached the mansion that housed the college, we heard a new—and to me, unfamiliar—sound. A sound that, to this day, some 70-odd years later, still lingers in my ears. The clear, young voices emanating from the college chapel, carried by the light evening breeze, sounded, to my unaccustomed ears, like the music of an angel choir.

In the relative stillness, the words, carried through the air from the open windows of the chapel, where Friday evening vespers heralded the beginning of the Sabbath, were plainly discernable:

"Jesus, Savior, pilot me
Over life's tempestuous sea
Unknown waves before me roll,
Hiding rock and treacherous shoal."*

New words to me then—now thoroughly familiar and beloved.

We continued our walk, were welcomed at the entrance, and joined the congregation of (mostly) young people as they proceeded with their evening worship.

As soon as was feasible, my sister and I found each other. I greeted her (typically) with tears. Mary (typically) pretended not to notice. She threw her arms around me. Then, the four little words—assurances—that had comforted and sustained me countless times throughout a somewhat tumultuous childhood: "I love you, Boo."

At some time during that weekend I decided, but kept to myself, that someday I would go to school in this place. I would sing with them at the beginning of another Sabbath day.

I told no one. But the Lord knew.

Against all odds, by the grace of God, I did just that. I entered Newbold College as a freshman several years later, only to leave after a month or two at the advent of World War II.

Seven years later the war was over—sort of—and I returned to Newbold. By this time I was a baptized member of the Seventh-day Adventist Church. I enrolled in the ministerial course, intending to become a minister. The Lord had other plans for me.

Approaching graduation, I told the Lord that I was willing to serve in whatever capacity He had in mind for me, wherever He wanted me.

Contrary to my expectations, He called me, soon after graduation, to teach—not to preach—at the boarding school for missionaries' children in Kenya, East Africa.

I taught students—from first grade through every grade, and, eventually, college-age and graduate students—for a total of around 50 years.

The years have not been without problems, of course, but I know that the Lord guided me into the wonderful field of education. I have had the incomparable privilege and honor and delight of spending most of my life "ministering" to, and being ministered to, by children and young people, surely very much among God's "chosen ones."

I would not change a moment of that experience. I love every one of those many, many young ones who have blessed me with their trust and sweet youthfulness. They taught me so much.

Above all else, I learned that, whether my students were 6 years old or 60 years old, they all, whether they realized it or not, needed, and longed for, the very same thing. They looked for acceptance. This is the gift of their heavenly Father to them.

I pray that I may, in a modest way, have reflected this, by His grace.

---

* *The Seventh-day Adventist Hymnal,* No. 551.

SHEILA: THREE WEEKS TO GRADUATION

She was tiny, even for a first-grader. She had short, jet-black hair and big expressive eyes, and she was terrified.

She was also very intelligent and quite enchanting.

For a combination of reasons, a mix of evangelical outreach and financial concerns, we had decided to recruit from the surrounding community a selected few pupils for our school for missionaries' children. Sheila was one of those selected.

Her father was a doctor from India. Her mother was Scottish. Sheila was a charming combination of the two races and cultures. She had not been to school before. Her family was introduced to us by a local Adventist doctor from the United States.

I had no knowledge of Sheila's religious or spiritual background—whether orthodox Hindu, or Christian, or a combination of the two, or neither. I just knew that I loved her on sight. I knew she was one of our Lord's special lambs—right now, a very frightened lamb.

The other children, almost all of whom were Seventh-day Adventists from birth and children of missionaries, were sophisticated, self-confident young people comfortable in their environment. They were also caring, responsive boys and girls, willing, even eager, to reach out to a little, timid "outsider."

I had prepared them for her coming. During our morning worship in the hostel—it was a boarding school—we had "introduced" Sheila, in absentia, and prayed for her and her family. The children had pledged their support in our effort to help her feel accepted and comfortable. Sheila, though, knew none of this. Very much a little fish out of water, she knew only that she didn't know anybody, they were all so "different," and she was scared.

I prayed for guidance. I prayed for her. I prayed for myself. I prayed for the other children. I prayed that the sweet Spirit would speak to this little one and calm her very evident fears.

Her mother brought her into the schoolroom. Clearly not entirely confident herself, Sheila's mom, not without difficulty, untangled her tiny daughter from her clasp and fled.

I knew she was crying. She had company.

Sheila stood there, silent, but with tears forming in her beautiful, dark eyes and rolling down her cheeks.

She looked so incredibly tiny, so defenseless, so utterly vulnerable. I prayed silently for guidance. I wanted, more than anything, to hold her, to assure her—with words I didn't have—that she was safe, that no one was going to hurt her, that we loved her.

So I did just that. I signaled to one of the older girls to take charge for a moment; then I put my arms around the shivering little girl, picked her up, and carried her to the front of the classroom.

One of the children brought me a chair, and I sat down, with tiny, terrified Sheila clinging to me with all her strength, and we just sat, crying together, for several minutes.

After a while, finding that nothing very terrible was happening to her, Sheila stopped crying, loosened her grip just a bit, and became, minimally at first, more relaxed. I never stopped praying, and it got easier. The children were wonderful. They were wholly supportive and understanding. School continued.

I taught school for three weeks with Sheila on my lap.

Quite calm fairly soon, at least on the surface, she, nevertheless, vehemently declined to vacate the one place where, apparently, she felt safe. The little fish was not quite ready to swim on her own. So the two of us "taught school" together. Surprisingly quickly, it began to feel almost "normal."

Inevitably, with the inducible cooperation of the rest of the school population, we convinced Sheila that she was beautiful, that she was precious, that we loved her, and that she was one of us, and she joined the school family and, eventually, fit in beautifully. Everyone adored her. Her mother admitted that she hadn't really believed it would work.

Actually, of course, the "convincing" was the work of the Holy Spirit, that member of the Godhead who speaks and understands Hindu, English,

Scottish, and every language known to humans, and, even more important, is able to interpret and respond to the tears and trembling of a terrified 6-year-old.

To be absolutely honest, I missed having Sheila on my lap and was secretly sort of sorry—in a way—when she "graduated."

FATHERS AND SONS

Two months isn't enough time to acclimate from urban England to semi-urban East Africa. Besides, I was a teacher—not a preacher—and was totally unprepared for the two young Kikuyu boys who came running up the driveway of the Seventh-day Adventist boarding school for missionaries' children near Nairobi, Kenya, early one Friday afternoon.

They told me—at least I thought they told me—that there was urgent need of a preacher, a Christian preacher, because someone had died. It appeared that a baby boy had died in the local African hospital, that the young mother was anxious for her child to have a Christian burial, and that her husband, although not himself a Christian, was equally anxious to comply with his wife's wishes.

The young wife was still confined to her hospital bed, and the husband had reportedly gone from church to church, from office to office, in an attempt to find someone willing to perform the rites that had suddenly assumed such significance.

Unfortunately, it was Friday afternoon. Few were at home or in their offices, and the young father was becoming increasingly desperate. The funeral had to take place that afternoon before the cemetery closed for the weekend. Otherwise, the baby would be taken from him by the public health authorities and disposed of. No man wants his son, no matter how new, disposed of.

But it was Friday afternoon. I had commitments at my school later in the evening. Although I held a ministerial license, I was a teacher, not a preacher. The minister was away on safari and could not be reached. I had never in my life conducted a funeral. I knew very little Swahili and no Kikuyu at all.

I immediately thought of a half dozen good reasons I couldn't possibly comply with the request. None, however, was half so compelling as the big eyes of the two Kikuyu youngsters, the beads of perspiration on their foreheads, and their pleading, "Won't you come, Bwana? Bwana, please come."

I slipped on my jacket hurriedly, thrust my Swahili Bible, which I could read but not understand, into my pocket, and accompanied the boys down the driveway, calling out to our houseboy to tell my wife where I had gone—which he promptly forgot to do.

On the way out of the compound I endeavored to compose my scattered thoughts, rummaging through the vague assorted impressions of funerals I had attended over the years, and tried to think of what else I would need to conduct one.

I had my Bible. The only other prerequisite that came to mind was flowers. Of course, flowers. Telling the boys to wait a minute, I doubled back and dodged through the hole in the hedge separating the school compound from the house of Dr. Mann, a Polish veterinary surgeon and our next-door neighbor.

I have no idea what the good doctor's servants thought as they saw me helping myself to various flowers from the garden. The family was out, and the servants probably felt that there must be some explanation. They adopted the locally common and, I think, eminently wise philosophy of not interfering with that which they did not immediately understand.

I rejoined my young companions, and we set out for the cemetery afoot. I had no car. The red dust was coating my brown leather shoes and exploding up in little bursts between the bare toes of my guides.

After a fairly long walk, we reached the African cemetery, and the boys led me to a relatively secluded corner where a knot of Africans was gathered. They were told, to my dismay, that the preacher was here.

Hastily and earnestly denying any pretensions of being a preacher, I made my way over to a somewhat distraught-looking young man standing off by himself. Evidently the father, he had tearstains on his face and was making low moaning sounds from time to time as if he were in pain.

I introduced myself to him and told him that while I was no preacher, I would, if he so wished, do the best that I could to conduct a suitable funeral service for his infant son.

I was unprepared for his gratitude. He seized both my hands in his own and began to weep afresh. With many interjections of *"Asante sana, Bwana* (Thank you very much, sir)," he told me, in a mixture of Swahili and English, that he was a dresser (aide) in the African hospital, and that his 8-day-old son—his first—had died that morning.

He told me that his wife was very sick and that he didn't know if she would live. He told me that he had promised her that their child would have a Christian burial, although he himself was not a Christian. Upon imparting this final item of information, he took a renewed grip on my hands, as if fearful I would run away and leave him.

Just across the hillside, two or three of his friends, Kikuyu tribesmen, were halfheartedly digging a grave with their pangas—long, broad-bladed knives that a Kikuyu uses for all purposes, from hoeing corn to cutting off heads when the occasion calls for it.

The father took me by the hand and led me to where the women were congregated beside a box. He wanted me to see his son.

"Gilbey's Gin" read the lettering stenciled on the rough wooden box. "Gilbey's Gin—London." And on the lid: "Gilbey's Reigns Supreme." And for all I know about gin—which is nothing—maybe it does.

It wasn't a very big box. Constructed to hold perhaps six bottles of gin for export, it was big enough, nevertheless, to hold the tiny body of the baby boy.

The father didn't have so much as a piece of cloth to wrap around the baby, and the child lay there in his gin-box casket looking just as he must have looked soon after he was born, perfect and beautiful, except that the cord that had bound him to his mother had gone and he was quite alone.

The women wailed, the father wept, and I, who was not supposed to cry because I was a White man and an Englishman, took a flower from the bouquet, which I had forgotten I was carrying, and laid it gently within the tiny, curled fingers.

It transpired that two "sermons" were expected, one around the "casket" and the second at the graveside. I saw that the ceremony must get under way if we were to beat the deadline of cemetery closing time.

With the aid of an English-speaking bystander, I gathered the mourners around the casket and gave my flowers to the women to hold. Standing beside the father, I pulled my Bible from my pocket. His eyes were fixed on the casket, which now had the lid nailed down and continued to proclaim for all to see that "Gilbey's Reigns Supreme."

I don't remember now what I said. I am not sure that I even knew at the time. I spoke in English, and somebody translated what I said into Swahili, and somebody else into Kikuyu. I read what I felt to be appropriate passages from my Swahili Bible. The father never took his eyes off the casket.

When I had run out of things to say, the father indicated that he and I should carry the casket across to the grave for the interment. We each took one end of the pathetically light little box and walked slowly across the red earth to the graveside, followed by the mourners and several spectators who had happened by.

I could see immediately that the shallow grave was not nearly deep enough to accommodate the tiny casket. The gravediggers had wearied of their task and gone off to rest somewhere.

No one appeared eager to provide any manual assistance, so the father and I commandeered a panga apiece from a couple of the bystanders and set to work to deepen the grave. I gave my jacket to one of the mourners to hold, and in about 20 minutes we had a hole deep enough to serve the purpose.

Somewhat to my surprise, no one had left, so I began the second part of the ceremony. Those who had drifted into the shade to rest gathered around, and I began to speak again.

My Bible was in my jacket pocket, and I had already read all the verses that seemed appropriate to me, anyway. So I spoke directly to the father, who was holding the casket in his arms, and told him what was in my heart. I could offer him no explanation and not much by way of immediate comfort. All I could do was take him by the hand and weep with him and tell him that somehow I understood how he felt.

And suddenly I began to know with my heart what I had always known with my head—that our heavenly Father made us brothers. Then I offered a prayer to the Father of us all.

There was only one untoward incident. When it came time to lower the little casket into the grave, the father was unwilling to let it go. He clutched it to him, and two of the mourners had to pry it loose from his grasp. Then we lowered it into the grave, and somebody covered it up with earth and stones.

The young father, whose name I never knew, got up from the ground, where he had lain sobbing, when he saw I was about to leave. He took my hands and wept and said, *"Asante sana, Bwana"* several times before he let me go.

The people dispersed quickly. It was almost curfew time. All I could see as I looked back was the tiny mound on the horizon with the bouquet of flowers on top that Dr. Mann didn't know he had sent for a Kikuyu baby's funeral.

In the confusion of my departure from home, I had neglected to provide myself with any money, so I could not take a car or even a bus. It was getting quite late by this time, and I lost my way. I have spent a considerable portion of my time getting lost, however, so this did not cause me undue concern.

I inquired the way of several passersby, and the last man of whom I requested directions was a tall, rather fierce-looking Kikuyu who obviously had no confidence in my ability to find my way unaided. He insisted on accompanying me to my driveway and refused to wait while I attempted to procure a monetary reward for his services.

My wife, who had long been of the opinion that if she let me out of her sight I would get into trouble, met me at the door. Her eyes wide at my mud-spattered, somewhat disheveled appearance, she inquired not unreasonably where I had been and what on earth I had been doing. I told her I had been digging a grave, and went inside to wash up.

I didn't often think of my bereaved Kikuyu friend, at least not consciously, during the next several years. He and his infant son were brought to mind a year or two later, however, as I hurried out of the railway station and across Waterloo Bridge in London, England.

I was on my way to visit my own son, Adrian, now almost 4 years old, who was in The Hospital for Sick Children on Great Ormond Street. Adrian was dying from leukemia.

I am something of a compulsive reader. I read bus tickets, railway timetables, discarded newspapers, anything with words printed on it—even posters.

"Gilbey's Gin," the poster read in letters three feet high. "Gilbey's Reigns Supreme." My eyes filled with tears. I think I was crying for all four of us.

One or two passersby glanced at me curiously and quickly looked away. Being English, they pretended not to notice anything unusual in my behavior. I could have stopped and explained to them, but I had things to do and much to say and very little time.

I thought of my nameless Kikuyu friend again as we laid our small son to rest in the little Thames Valley graveyard. He couldn't know, of course. But I knew that if I had needed any flowers stolen, any gravedigging done, or just someone to take my hand and mingle his tears with mine, if he could have known, and if it had been possible, he would have been there.

CHOMBA

When he asked me, just as I was about to hear him say his bedtime prayer, "Daddy, is Chomba a Christian?" I didn't know how to answer him.

He was 3 years old, and Chomba was his favorite among all the African staff at the East African boarding school. Oh, yes, he liked old Isaac, the cook, and Isaac watched over him and cared for him as well as any nursemaid. He liked to watch Nzorka, the gardener, and would follow him around as he went about his work, although he was a tiny bit afraid of him. But it was Chomba, the Kikuyu houseboy, to whom he had grown the closest.

Perhaps it was because Chomba was the youngest of all the Kikuyu tribesmen who were part of the school family. Or perhaps it was because of Chomba's ready smile and never-failing cheerfulness. In fact, the young houseboy's readiness to "go the second mile" without even being asked had endeared him to us all. Whatever the reason, whenever Adrian ("Ady," for short) was not immediately in evidence and a search was organized to determine his whereabouts (which took place, on the average, six or seven times a day), the inevitable suggestion was: "Go see what Chomba's doing. Ady's probably with him." And nine times out of 10 he was.

To return to the original question concerning Chomba's qualifications for inclusion with those who professed to follow our Lord, the problem was a bit more complex than it appeared on the surface. For instance, there was the matter of his two wives. A problem for a Solomon, to be sure.

The mission-trained help had, unfortunately, proved unsatisfactory, and it had become necessary to recruit from outside the Christian community if our school was to remain operative. Consequently, our domestic staff was comprised wholly of non-Christian Kikuyu tribesmen. This, we realized, was less than ideal. But they were willing, cheerful, and industrious, and were therefore pearls of great price not to be lightly relinquished.

Chomba and I discussed the situation as soon as I was aware that he had moved into his little room in the servants' quarters with his two attractive young wives and tiny baby son.

"Look here, Chomba," I told him, "you must realize that you cannot have two wives here. I recognize that it is tribal custom and perfectly legitimate within your society, but it is contrary to Christian belief and practice."

"But Bwana," Chomba objected apologetically, "they are *both* my wives. I married them both in good faith. I can't just throw one out. What would she do? Where would she go?" A couple of good questions if ever there were any.

Finally we agreed on a compromise. Chomba was to maintain one wife at a time in his quarters at the school. He was to send the other one back to his home in his village in the highlands. Then, if they wanted to "trade off" at intervals, that would be all right with me.

I didn't think that anyone other than Chomba and myself was aware that the smiling young face hovering over the cooking fire outside Chomba's room in the evening did not always belong to the same young woman. To most, an African was an African, and a servant's wife was not the sort of individual to merit much attention.

Adrian knew, though. He used to visit Chomba in his little room and play with his baby, and he quickly learned the names—and the faces—of the folk who lived in the servants' quarters. "Chomba's other mummy came today, Daddy," he informed me. "She's nice."

It was Chomba who first drew my attention to the fact that Ady was not looking well. The little boy had been paler than usual for some days. His cheeks had lost some of their rosiness, and his boundless store of energy seemed strangely diminished.

"The *toto* (child) needs some *dawa* (medicine), Bwana," he suggested, somewhat diffidently.

After a little close observation, we were inclined to agree.

The doctor—a skilled and understanding pediatrician—asked a lot of questions, conducted a thorough examination, and scheduled blood and bone marrow tests. We took Ady home.

The results of the tests were to be ready Friday afternoon. School was out for the day, and I sat in the empty classroom, staring blankly at the half-cleaned chalkboard and trying to control the trembling of my hands. I had wept some, had prayed a lot, and was deathly afraid.

While in college I had worked as an aide in a big general hospital in England, and the nature of the tests being performed told my mind what my heart refused to believe. I had cared for leukemia patients on a number of occasions.

The doctor came to the house to deliver the results of the tests personally. We did our best to spare each other, but the tears would not be held back.

In a tight-knit little community such as ours, news—good or bad—travels fast. Chomba sought me out in the empty classroom later that evening. I heard his soft-voiced *"Hodi!"* ["Is anyone there?"] behind me, but I did not turn my head. He walked up to where I sat in the shadows, his bare feet making no sound on the wooden floor. He stood silent behind my chair for several moments.

When he spoke I could tell by his voice that there were tears in his eyes. He put his hand on my shoulder and spoke in Swahili: "Oh, Bwana," he said, his voice husky with grief, "our son must die." He began to weep quietly.

It was some months—months that seemed like years—and many miles later that I realized what it was that Chomba had said. *"Our* son . . . " he had said. "Our son must die."

I thought of that conference in heaven, millenniums ago and untold miles distant, when the provision had been made that ensured that those who went to sleep in Jesus would rise again. I thought of the love of the heavenly family that had decided—for love of me—that another Son must die. I marveled—and was humbled by the wonder of it all.

If my little son were here now, and if he were to ask me again if Chomba was a Christian, I think I would know how to reply.

THE MARBLE AND THE SHELL

Adrian sat very straight on the horsehair sofa. He had his hands thrust deep into his trouser pockets, and his legs were dangling. His legs were dangling because it was quite a high sofa, and he had his hands in his pockets because he liked the feel of the things he had in there.

He had a marble in his left-hand pocket and a shell in his right-hand pocket. But it was not an ordinary marble; it was a big glass one. It was red and yellow and green and blue, and the colors were kind of inside the marble, as if they were a part of the glass. He had held it close to his eyes a good many times and looked right inside it, and he wondered how the colors were put in that way. He must remember to ask Daddy about it.

The shell had a hard Latin name that his daddy had told him—he couldn't remember it now. Anyway, he did know that it was a very beautiful shell. It was curly, and the outside was pale yellow with brown speckles on it, and the inside was a sort of whitish pink—like his baby sister's fingernails.

He had found it himself back in Africa, on the shores at Mombasa. When the waves washed it up out of the ocean right at his feet, he had picked it up, washing it in a pool, and had run to show it to his daddy. If you held it to your ear, you could hear the waves roaring in up the beach.

The nurse was coming along the corridor now with a handful of brown cards. She had a blue-striped dress with a white apron and a stiff white collar and cuffs, and she had a frilly white cap on her head. She gave one of the cards to every mommy or daddy with a child.

All of the nurses here were White people; even the men who were polishing the floors and running messages were White. Adrian wasn't quite sure whether he liked this country so well. It seemed to be a terribly rainy sort of place, and he hadn't really felt warm since he got off the plane last Wednesday. But it was his country. He had been born here. He knew that. And, as Daddy said, you couldn't get used to a place in two days. Adrian thought it would probably be all right, because it was his daddy's country too.

The man in the white coat smiled down at the small boy. Adrian was glad he didn't say "It won't hurt," because that was a lie. Adrian poked the third finger of his right hand toward the man. It was a little grubby—and it was warm, too, from holding his shell. He liked the feel of the cold stuff the man rubbed on his finger, but he didn't like the sharp prick of the needle. He winced a little, but he didn't squeal or pull his hand away, because his daddy had asked him to try not to.

"Good fellow," said the man in the white coat, and passed him on to the woman at the bench with the little glass bottles and the rubber tube in her mouth.

The bright-red blood creeping up the tube fascinated Adrian. He was glad the woman didn't ask him his name or how old he was, as some of them did. He knew perfectly well that all that was written down on the card on her bench, and he liked to watch the blood run down the glass part of the tubing into the little bottle. How bright and pretty it was. He wondered whether you were full of it inside or if it was just in your fingers. The woman finished, took a breath, and smiled at him.

"Thank you. Please may I go now?" asked Adrian, letting go of Daddy's hand to adjust the bit of cotton she had stuck on his finger.

"Thank *you,*" said the woman. "Yes, that's all." And she smiled at him again.

The leather-covered seat in the ward waiting room wasn't quite so high as the one in the outpatients' department, and Adrian's feet almost reached the floor. He had enjoyed his dinner very much. He always liked eating in a restaurant. There were so many interesting things to see. He thought about the man at the table across the aisle and how he had shoveled his dinner into his mouth. Adrian supposed his mother hadn't ever taught him the proper way to eat. Or maybe, because he was so old, he had forgotten. Or maybe he hadn't eaten for days and days—perhaps even a week.

I'LL HOLD YOU WHILE IT HURTS

He was vaguely aware of the tall doctor standing talking to his daddy in a corner of the room.

"You realize, Mr. Milward," the doctor was saying, "the seriousness of the situation. As of this moment, there is nothing really we can do—we can only relieve . . . six months, perhaps, maybe less, maybe more. It is impossible to say. But at the moment, anyway, until we can get some sort of reaction pattern established, I'm afraid we must insist . . ."

Adrian supposed they were talking about him. Daddy had told him that perhaps he would have to stay in the hospital for a while, that he must be as brave as he possibly could, and had promised to come and see him every day.

The doctor was coming across to speak to him, so Adrian stood up. The doctor and Daddy were both smiling at him, but Daddy's smile was kind of a crooked one—like when you have fallen down and have to have iodine put on your knee.

"Come on, old man," said Daddy, taking such a tight hold of his hand that it hurt his fingers. "Let's go and find Sister Scott. She's going to look after you for a little while."

Sister Scott had blue eyes, gray hair, and glasses. She looked very kind, and she reminded Adrian of the woman who used to talk to him across the road in the garden of the Greek Orthodox church in Nairobi. She walked on the other side of him and held his other hand as they went to find his bed in a corner of the glass-enclosed ward.

There were four or five other children there already, but Adrian hardly noticed them. He was having a little difficulty with his top lip, and his eyes were inclined to water a little today. He must remember that he was 3 years old now.

But it was going to be all right. Daddy had said that it was going to be all right.

Adrian swallowed hard and marched up to his bed in the corner. He had both hands thrust deep into his pockets now. In the left-hand pocket was a marble, and in the right-hand pocket was a shell.

"SING FOR ME"

In addition to my son, Adrian, there were seven children in his ward at The Hospital for Sick Children in London. They ranged from Adrian's almost 4 years of age, through Carolyn, Elizabeth, Joseph, Hermie, Miriam, and Sally, to 12-year-old Freddie.

All of the young patients were victims of leukemic diseases and didn't have long to live. All, that is, except one—beautiful, green-eyed, golden-haired Elizabeth, who was 10 years old. After completing a common regimen of therapy with the other children, she would go home to live a healthy life.

Yet the other children felt a genuine and profound sympathy for the little girl, as I learned when I paid my daily visits to my son and talked—not only with him but with the others. Companions in distress, the children shared everything—even their parents.

Elizabeth, who had undergone complicated surgery in the region behind her ears, was going deaf. The process was quite advanced, and it would be only a matter of months before her hearing loss was complete—and irreversible. That Elizabeth was an ardent music lover, who possessed a clear and delightful singing voice and showed promise as a pianist, made the prospect of her inevitable deafness all the more tragic.

But she never complained. Occasionally, though, when she thought no one was looking, silent tears would form in her eyes and slowly roll down her cheeks.

Elizabeth loved music more than anything else, and she enjoyed listening as much as she enjoyed performing. Frequently, after I had helped my son prepare for bed, she would beckon me into the playroom, which was quiet after the day's activities. Seating herself in a big, leather armchair, and making room for me to sit beside her, she would take my hand and say, "Sing for me."

Certainly no Pavarotti, but capable of carrying a tune, I could not deny her request. Facing her so she could see my lips, and enunciating as clearly as I could, I would sing a couple of songs for these special "command performances." She would listen intently and with obvious enjoyment, then thank me gravely with a quick kiss on the forehead.

The other children, as I have said, were disturbed by the little girl's plight and decided to do something to cheer her up. Under Freddie's leadership they came to a decision, which they took to staff nurse Hilda Kirby.

"Kirby," as she was know to parents and children alike, was a tall, angular young woman, whose formidable manner had been known to strike terror in the casual observer. The children, however, were not deceived by her brusque efficiency. They knew that Kirby was their friend.

Initially, Kirby was taken aback by their announcement. "You want to give a concert for Elizabeth's eleventh birthday?" she exclaimed. "And it's in three weeks' time? You're mad."

Upon seeing their crestfallen faces, she added, "You're all mad. But I'll help you."

Kirby lost no time in keeping her promise. She hurried to the telephone in the nurses' sitting room and dialed the number of a conservatory of music, not a great distance away in north London. "Kindly give a message to Sister Mary Joseph," she instructed the receptionist. "Tell her to expect a visit this evening from Hilda Kirby on important business."

As soon as she was off duty, Kirby took a cab to the conservatory to see her friend, Sister Mary Joseph, who was a voice and choir teacher.

After a brief greeting, the nun came right to the point. "Kirby," she asked, "what harebrained scheme do you intend to involve me in now?"

"Mary J," replied Kirby, "is it possible to transform a small group of children, none of whom has had any musical training, into a passable choir, capable of giving a concert in three weeks?"

"It is possible," replied Sister Mary Joseph. "Not very probable, but possible."

"Bless you, Mary J," exclaimed the nurse. "I knew you would."

"Just a minute, Kirby," said the bewildered nun. "Tell me more. Maybe I am unworthy of your blessing."

Twenty minutes later the two parted on the steps of the conservatory. "Bless you, Mary J," repeated Kirby. "We'll see you on Wednesday at 3:00."

"Called what?" demanded Freddie incredulously as Kirby confronted him and the other children while Elizabeth was undergoing her daily therapy. "Is she a man or a woman, then? How can she be called 'Mary Joseph'?"

"She's a nun, Freddie. She teaches at one of the best music schools in London. It'd cost you two guineas an hour to take lessons from her. And she's going to train you—for free."

"Blimey!" interjected Hermie, who knew the value of a shilling because his mother kept a stall in London's Sunday-morning market in Petticoat Lane. Brushing aside Freddie's objections, Hermie said, "We'll take it."

So it was settled. Under Sister Mary Joseph's able direction, the children practiced each day while Elizabeth was undergoing therapy. There was only one major problem: how to include 9-year-old Joseph in the concert. Clearly, Joseph could not be left out, but following surgery, he could no longer use his vocal cords.

"Joseph," the nun told him after she had noticed him watching wistfully as the others were assigned their singing parts, "I believe our Lord wants you to help me in a very special way at the concert. You have the same name as I have, and He wants you to work quite closely with me. You will sit beside me and turn the music pages as I play the piano."

For a brief moment Joseph's eyes shone. Then, close to tears, he scribbled frantically on his notepad, "But Sister, I can't read music."

Sister Mary Joseph smiled down at the anxious little boy. "Don't worry, Joseph," she assured him. "You will. Our Lord and I will work on it."

Incredibly, within the three-week deadline, the Lord, Sister Mary Joseph, and Kirby transformed six dying children, none of whom had any noticeable musical talent, into an acceptable choir, and a little boy who could neither sing nor speak into a confident page-turner.

Equally remarkable, the secret was well kept. Elizabeth's surprise as she was led into the hospital chapel on the afternoon of her birthday and seated on a "throne" (a wheelchair) was genuine. Her pretty face flushed with excitement, and she leaned forward to listen.

Although the audience—10 parents and three nurses—sat only a few feet from the platform, we had some difficulty in seeing the faces of the choristers clearly. But we didn't have any trouble hearing them as they worked through a somewhat incongruous repertoire that ranged from "Jesus Loves Me" to "Danny Boy"—all favorites of Elizabeth's.

"Remember to sing *loudly,"* Sister Mary Joseph had admonished the choristers just before the program began. "You know she can hear very little, so give it all you've got." And they did.

The concert was a great success. Elizabeth said it was the best birthday she had ever had. The choir almost burst with pride. Joseph beamed. The rest of us, I'm afraid, shed more tears.

Anyone who is close to desperately ill or dying children realizes that it is not the hopelessness of their situation, nor even their physical suffering, that is so devastating. It is their indomitability, their courage in the face of overwhelming odds, that breaks your heart.

I have no printed program to show for the most memorable of all the concerts I have attended. No rave reviews were written. Nevertheless, I have never heard, nor do I expect to hear, more beautiful music. If I close my eyes, I can still hear every note.

Those six young voices have been stilled now these many years. All seven members of the choir—the six young choristers and the silent page-turner—are sleeping. But I guarantee that Elizabeth, now married and the mother of her own golden-haired, green-eyed daughter, can still hear, in the ear of her memory, those six young voices that were among the last sounds she ever heard.

BEAUTIFUL UPON THE MOUNTAINS

She had neither red hair nor freckles, but somehow she made me think of a combination of Peppermint Patty and the little red-haired girl. She combined the same contrasting characteristics of indomitability and innocent appeal.

Certainly not a prepossessing child in physical appearance, she was, I suppose, 10 or 11 years old. It was difficult to be sure of her age from her appearance. Her somewhat stunted, malformed frame made her appear younger than she was, while her small, oval face most commonly wore an expression that would have seemed more at home on the face of a grown woman.

Her eyes were her dominant feature. Large, dark, and luminous, fringed by long, thick lashes, they were—at first sight—her one beauty. She had a singular habit of gazing steadily for a long moment at a newcomer to the children's ward. For some, this was disconcerting. It was almost as if she were looking through you rather than at you. If she liked what she saw, her face would light up and she would shuffle over to the approved one and introduce herself.

She had a smile, the nurses said, that could light up a room and could make you forget her misshapen body and painful, awkward method of locomotion.

She smiled often. I never saw her cry, although she was no stranger to pain, rejection, and disappointment. Valerie, I gathered, had already shed all her tears—several years and countless operations ago.

She would be a patient in the children's surgical ward for frequent, prolonged periods and then would disappear, only to return within a few months for further corrective surgery—surgery that could only, at best, make life viable for her, a child classified as afflicted with MBD (multiple birth defects).

I'LL HOLD YOU WHILE IT HURTS

Valerie had a well-developed—if slightly cynical—sense of humor. When some unthinking visitor would—inconceivably—ask her what was wrong with her, she would smile sweetly and suggest that they return later, when they had a day off and time to spare. "But," she would add innocently, "if you're in a hurry, I can tell you what's right with me."

Whenever she was recovering from one of her frequent operations, Valerie would "fall" out of her bed—that was the only way she could manage this feat without help, and she scorned help—and shuffle around the ward, helping out with the care of the other children.

In spite of Valerie's somewhat grotesque appearance and curious method of maneuvering, the other small patients always liked her. She could get them to do things when the nurses failed.

Valerie stood for no nonsense. Pain was a fact of life as far as she was concerned. From long and close acquaintance, she had come to terms with it, and she had, in her small, misshapen frame, enough courage for a wardful of other children who were, perhaps, making its acquaintance for the first time.

Valerie's parents didn't visit her every day, as many of the other children's parents did. Probably they were both working or had other children to care for. They came once or twice a week, and Valerie didn't seem to care desperately whether her mother came or not. A young, fashionably dressed woman, her mother frequently seemed to be in a hurry. She always gave an impression of embarrassment and sort of disassociated herself from her odd little daughter when other parents stopped by.

Valerie's father, on the other hand, was an outgoing, affectionate sort of person. He would wait at the end of the ward for Valerie to shuffle across to him, her face lit up like a lantern. He would always greet her in the same way. "Hi there, beautiful," he'd call, making it sound as if he really meant it. And, just for a moment, as the little girl would reach the end of her shuffling run toward him, drop her canes, and fall into his arms, he'd be right.

Then one cold, windy autumn night, Billy came onto the ward. Actually, it was very early in the morning, before dawn. He came up from emergency surgery following a three-car wreck on the M-2 expressway.

His parents were relatively unhurt, but Billy had been pinned in the wreckage for a long time and had sustained severe injuries to his lower legs.

The tentative prognosis was that 8-year-old Billy had taken his last steps. The doctors and nurses thought so. Billy's parents thought so. Billy himself was sunk in deep depression. He *knew* he would never walk again, let alone run, jump, play soccer, or do any of the other things that made his life worth living.

Valerie, however, had other ideas. After summing up the situation, she decided that the prognosis was nonsense. "The kid'll walk," she declared. Valerie spoke with authority. She had been there. She knew.

When, fairly well along in his convalescence, Billy still steadfastly refused to get out of bed, put his feet on the floor, and try to stand, Valerie took over his "case."

Not without considerable difficulty, she maneuvered her mobile walker over to his bedside immediately after breakfast one morning and issued her first—but not her last—directive. "Out of that bed, kid," she ordered. "It's time to get up."

Paying no attention to Billy's tearful protestations that he couldn't walk, and heedless of his demands that she go away and leave him alone, she, by sheer force of will, inveigled him out of his bed and into an upright position and, finally, into the walker.

It took her nine weeks—weeks of unrelenting, continuing perseverance—but she did it. She spent what must have been desperately exhausting hours with him every day. She refused to give up. At the end of the day she would crumple—quite literally—into an untidy heap on the floor, and would be asleep before a nurse came by to lift her onto her bed.

She put up with all kinds of abuse from her unwilling "patient." I saw her visibly rattled on only one occasion. Once, early on in the rehabilitation program, Billy, frustrated by his own slow progress, lost his temper and stormed at her, "Valerie, why can't you leave me alone? What do you know? You're weird."

Valerie stopped dead. Her little face went white and her chin quivered. She looked as close to tears as I ever saw her. But only for a moment. Then she stuck out her chin and fixed the red-faced boy with those eyes of hers.

"I know," she said, slowly and distinctly. "But I can't help it—and you can. Come on."

After that, things went better. Billy became more cooperative and, some weeks later, when he began to share her faith in his ultimate recovery, even enthusiastic.

Then, close to three months after he entered the hospital, Billy closed the curtains around his bed, dressed himself in the new suit his excited parents had brought, packed his "things" into his small suitcase, and walked—yes, walked—confidently around the ward to say goodbye.

We all—staff, parents, and ambulatory children—gathered at the window to wave at him as he walked with his parents to the parking lot out in front of the hospital. Valerie was there. Billy, grinning from ear to ear, turned and waved. We waved back. Valerie couldn't wave. She needed both hands on her canes to support herself. If she let go, she would fall over. Her face betrayed no sign of emotion, but her tiny knuckles as she clutched the hands of her walking canes were suddenly very white.

Many of us, watching the little tableau, could scarcely bear the contrast—the excited, happy little boy who had learned to walk again, and the tiny, misshapen little girl who would never walk properly. It was almost too much for us.

Billy got into the car with his parents and little sister, and with a final wave he was gone.

We stood staring out into the courtyard, unwilling to move.

Valerie was the first to speak. "Well," she said, "what are we all staring at? There's work to be done. Come on, it's time to get the trays 'round for supper."

Wait one moment: Did I call her the little girl who would never walk? Correction: She will walk. One day Valerie will walk straight and tall. She will walk without tiring, and she won't fall down. Please, God, may it be soon.

CAROLYN'S CHRISTMAS

She wouldn't smile at me today, Daddy," Adrian confided, a worried look in his gray eyes. "She seemed sad." And with a perception beyond his almost 4 years, "Maybe she's afraid she's not going to get better—not ever."

I glanced across the hospital ward toward Carolyn's bed. When I arrived to visit my small son, she would frequently come across to Ady's bed and join us and sit and chat for a while.

But not today. She was lying—fully dressed—on her bed, curled into a ball, with her back toward the other occupants of the ward. Clearly, right now Carolyn didn't feel like talking to anyone.

"You're probably right," I assured Adrian. "She's most likely not feeling good today. Maybe she'll be feeling better tomorrow." And I left it at that, because another problem that demanded my attention had come up. This problem, too, concerned Carolyn.

I had been visiting the terminal ward at The Hospital for Sick Children in London to see my little boy so regularly and for so long that I had come to feel like—and to be treated almost as—a member of the staff. So when it came time to plan for the ward Christmas party and the problem came up, the Sister and staff nurse in charge of the ward sought my opinion.

They were aware that I was a Christian and a Seventh-day Adventist, and they knew I had been a missionary, so I suppose they felt that I was therefore somehow qualified to provide a ruling on what was, in effect, sort of a theological question.

The problem concerned Carolyn and the forthcoming Christmas party. Carolyn, you see, was Jewish. Her parents were Orthodox, and she never accompanied the other children to the hospital chapel on Sunday evenings for the church service.

Would it be proper, queried Sister Palmer, for Carolyn to attend the Christmas party? It was, after all, a Christian celebration. Did I think her parents would object? And if she didn't attend, what should be done with her while the party was in progress?

The nurses were not wholly satisfied with my comments. It would not, I pointed out, be a religious-type party. And, to my mind, a much more important question was whether Carolyn herself wanted to be there or not.

As I said, the nurses were not fully convinced that I had the solution, so for the time being the question was left open. I returned to the ward to help my little son get ready for bed before I had to leave for home 40 miles away.

Several days passed. Each day, as I visited the hospital and talked with my little boy, I saw Carolyn. She seemed about the same as usual—a bit depressed perhaps, but that was to be expected.

Carolyn was the oldest of the eight children currently in the terminal ward. None of them could reasonably anticipate much of a future, but most of the boys and girls were too young to realize their situation fully.

Carolyn, however, was 10 years old—going on 11—and she had a pretty good idea of what was in store for her. A victim of a leukemic-type disease, she had overheard enough to realize that her prospects were—to put it conservatively—not bright.

Three or four days after Adrian's initial observation of her evident depression, Carolyn joined us in the early evening as I was putting Ady to bed before leaving to catch my train. I noted the dark shadows under her eyes. She looked desperately tired.

I knew little of the progress of her disease. Only what I had heard—and overheard—from the conversation of the doctors and nurses. The chart at the foot of each child's bed was an identification chart only. All the data it bore was the name, age, sex, and religion (if any) of the child, together with the name of the doctor in charge. All the pertinent information concerning the diagnosis, progress of his or her condition, and prognosis was filed away from prying eyes in Sister's office.

Carolyn pulled my head down to her level where she sat on the edge of Adrian's bed and spoke into my ear. Ady was just dropping off to sleep. "Can you stay and talk to me a little while when Ady's asleep?" she requested. "Will you, please?"

I was on the point of telling her that I really had to leave to catch my train home. Something in her face, however, stopped me. She had a look of despair in her big, dark eyes—a desperate look I found almost terrifying in one so young.

"All right," I agreed. "As soon as Ady's really sleeping. Give me a minute to call home, and I'll be with you."

I went to the nurses' sitting room and phoned home. I assured my wife that Ady was all right—that there was no change. I told her that something had come up and I would have to get a later train than usual. She was not to worry. I would explain when I saw her.

I returned to the ward where Carolyn awaited me. She looked relieved, almost as if she had feared I would not return.

"Thank you," she said. "I've got to talk to somebody or I'll burst. Daddy's away again in Switzerland on a business trip, and Mummy always bursts into tears if I say anything except 'I feel fine.'"

I nodded. I had met Carolyn's parents briefly when their visits to the hospital had coincided with mine. Her father, a tall, distinguished-looking man, was one of those parents who was totally unable to accept what was happening to his only daughter. He evidently, I gathered, felt that by denying the unthinkable, he would make it go away. He was frequently away in Europe on business. Her mother was an affectionate, emotional sort of person. They both obviously adored their daughter.

I secured a wheelchair and wheeled Carolyn into the now empty playroom adjoining the ward. Toys were still strewn around the floor from the afternoon's activities. I swept a couple of plush rabbits and a teddy bear from a leather-covered armchair, carefully lifted Carolyn into my arms, and settled her into the armchair. I drew up another chair and sat down close to her.

For a minute or two neither of us spoke.

I can never forget what I saw: a slender figure in a blue, lace-trimmed robe and, incongruously, pink slippers. She looked lost, almost, in the big armchair, and terribly, unbearably vulnerable. Her dark, luminous eyes were fixed earnestly on mine. Two big tears escaped and rolled slowly down her cheeks.

I leaned forward involuntarily and took both her hands in my own. I didn't know quite what to say. "Well, Carolyn," I began inanely, "it won't be long now till Christmas."

She looked at me almost uncomprehendingly. "I don't care about Christmas," she assured me, almost fiercely. "Christmas is for Christians, anyway."

I realized suddenly that I had nothing to say that Carolyn wanted to hear. She needed—desperately needed—a listener.

The words came slowly at first—haltingly—as if she were dragging them up from who knows what unknown depths. She held onto my hands, and soon the words began to pour out, faster and faster. A deluge—a torrent of words.

She told me about her home, her parents, her grandmother, her cat and dog, vacation trips to Spain, to Switzerland, to the Riviera.

She told me of her "Christmas"—of the celebration of the eight days of Hanukkah. Her eyes shone as she told me of her grandmother lighting the menorah—the nine-branched candelabrum—of the songs and prayers that accompanied the Jewish celebration. She released my hands and gesticulated as she recounted the ancient story of the liberation of the Jewish people by the heroic Maccabeans.

I listened—mesmerized almost—and my thoughts turned to dogs, and Phoenician women, and crumbs.

Suddenly her mood changed. Exhausted, she sank back in her chair, and her voice became almost a whisper. "I know," she said, her voice breaking. "I know I'm going to die."

Her tears fell freely now. "You know," she said between sobs, "I can't believe it, but I know it's true. You know," she said again, "I want to have a boyfriend. I want a boy to tell me he loves me and can't live without me. I want to grow up and get married. I want to have children of my own. I want to live." Her voice broke.

She threw her long, dark hair back from her face and looked straight at me, her small fists clenched, willing me to do something about it.

She gave a despairing yelp—I don't know what else to call it—like a small animal caught in a trap, and threw herself into my arms. "I don't want to die," she wailed.

What does one say to a 10-year-old girl who doesn't want to die?

I held her close to me and stroked her shining dark hair. I told her she was beautiful. I wept along with her and felt totally inadequate.

She didn't say any more. She clung to me, sobbing, for a long time.

After a while she quieted down and, finally, fell asleep with her head on my shoulder. I called for a nurse, and together we carried her back to the ward and put her in her bed. I tried to compose myself and washed my face in cold water before I left for the railroad depot and my train home. It was late by this time. Adrian was still fast asleep.

When I visited my little son the following afternoon, I saw immediately that the bed across from Ady's—Carolyn's bed—was occupied by a little boy. He was about 7 years old. He told me his name was Jimmy.

I asked no questions, and nobody made any comment. It wasn't that sort of ward. Nobody—not even the youngest—ever asked why a bed was suddenly empty or occupied by a newcomer. Everybody—even the youngest—sensed it was something that nobody could bear to talk about.

Later, however, Sister Palmer drew me to one side and told me that Carolyn had lived only halfway through the night.

"Her mother and grandmother were there," she told me in answer to my question. "Her father was in Geneva on business. We phoned, but of course he didn't arrive in time."

I saw Carolyn's parents once more just a couple of days later as I was arriving to visit my son. They were just leaving. They had evidently been up to the ward to collect what lawyers refer to as "the effects." Her father, who looked stunned, carried a small blue suitcase. Her mother, who was weeping, looked for all the world like a small child who had just been scolded. She dangled a flaxen-haired doll by one leg.

I bowed slightly as they approached. The mother put out a hand as if to detain me. The father set down the suitcase and took both my hands. "You're Ady's father," he said in his heavily accented English. "Carolyn spoke of you. Thank you." His eyes filled with tears. I bowed again. There was nothing to say.

So Carolyn missed the Christmas party after all. Most of the parents were there, and everyone studiously worked at having a good time. To be fair, the little ones did have fun, I am sure.

There was a tree, and Santa Claus, carols, games, lots of ice cream and cookies, and records playing "Rudolph the Red-nosed Reindeer." There really wasn't much mention of Jesus or religion at all.

I wondered what Carolyn would have thought of it.

A GARLAND OF CHILDREN

Some children's eyes, clouded with pain,
Will not see Christmastime again
Dear Jesus weeps and understands
He reaches out to hold their hands

Lord, does he really have to go?
I don't know how this can be so
It cannot be Your holy will
That small ones should be sick and ill

Lord, bless these nurses, always there
Providing tender, loving care
To wipe a brow, to soothe a fear
To lessen pain, to wipe a tear

We thank You, dear sweet Lord above
These small ones came to show Your love
An all too brief, but precious, loan
We give them back; they are Your own

I do not ask to understand
But please, Lord, hold onto my hand

The Hospital for Sick Children,
Great Ormond Street, London,
March 1956

"A TIME TO KEEP SILENCE"

In actual fact, I didn't really recall it was still in my possession. I have "lost" so many things over the years—things I had put away in a "safe place"—and was currently searching for something entirely different.

But when I came across it and, not without wonder, carefully unwrapped the white tissue paper—yellowing now—it took me back more than 40 years and across a continent and an ocean.

Even at 10 years old, Sheila was unforgettable. She had an indefinable quality that, once you got to know her, grabbed you and would not let go.

Paradoxically, perhaps because she was a patient in the terminal ward of a famed children's hospital in London, England, the quality that immediately drew people to her was that she was so "alive."

Clearly, Sheila enjoyed living; unhappily, she wasn't going to have very much more time for enjoyment.

We all knew it: the nurses and doctors, the parents—of whom I was one—who visited their own children, her mother.

Sheila knew it too.

In and out of the ward daily for about a year, I began to talk with—or more often listen to—Sheila while my little boy slept. Their beds were close to each other.

Sheila was interested in everything. An intelligent and well-read child, she was ready to talk about anything and everything. We talked about animals—she had a dog and a cat. We talked about flowers—she had a small garden at home. We branched out into literature, art, music, and philosophy—within the limitations of our mutual experience, of course.

I came to realize that, consciously or not, Sheila was attempting to build a sort of indestructible infrastructure for herself. She was trying to devise some sort of immortality.

For building blocks she was using her recollections of experiences that had brought her to where she was and her concepts of experiences that she longed for but knew she would never achieve.

As we got to know each other better, we tentatively—she was a remarkably sensitive child—talked some about Ady, my own little son, who was almost 4 years old. Sometimes we shared tears.

Eventually, of course, we talked about religion. Having had a fairly orthodox exposure to religion, Sheila, in common with the majority of the population, had a rather hazy concept of the Godhead, of just where she was in the order of things.

But as weeks went by and hope—which was never really hope, anyway—faded, she began to think about, and talk about, her concept of heaven and life after death.

"I expect I shall have wings," she confided to me one evening. "I suppose I will be able to fly all around heaven, which is even more beautiful than Cornwall." She had spent her last vacation on the Cornish coast in the west of England.

"And of course there will be animals. Maybe even Tabby and Oscar will be there, too, after they die. And there will be flowers everywhere."

There was more. We discussed it at length.

While I held somewhat of a different view of the state of the dead immediately after dying, there was no way I was going to deprive Sheila of the comfort she derived from knowing that she would fly from her grave into the arms of the waiting angels, even if I was to be condemned for silence. The difference, I told myself, was essentially only in one's concept of time.

Some days, of course, were worse than others. For every occupant of the ward, whether 3 years old or 13, the very worst day was when they were due for another bone marrow aspiration. This procedure involved the insertion of a very large and quite terrifying needle into the spinal area to withdraw bone marrow for inspection so as to determine the progress of their leukemic-type diseases. It was very painful.

It was supposed to be a secret until the actual time for the procedure arrived, but schedules were "leaked," and the older children, at least, could pretty well figure out when the fairly regularly scheduled appointments were due.

"Tomorrow," said Sheila, grabbing onto me with tears welling up in her eyes, "is going to be needle day."

We didn't talk much that evening. She just hung onto me, and I prayed and wished so much that I could have the procedure in her place.

A lot of the time, though, I read to her. She had lots of books.

One evening I had to have two tries at entering the ward. I stood in the doorway and looked across at my little boy. He didn't know, but I knew, and Sheila knew, too, that the next day was to be "needle day" for him. I had to beat a retreat and compose myself a bit before giving it another try.

Later that evening I was trying to read to Sheila. Unfailingly polite and very careful with the language she used, she suddenly turned and almost glared at me. Her eyes were full of tears. "Put the d—— book down," she said. "Why don't you just hold me?"

I did as I was told.

A little later, just before I left for home, she took both my hands in her small ones. "Oh," she said, "it must be devastating for you."

(I told you she read a great deal.)

I didn't know her mother very well. A reserved person, she was always friendly when our visits coincided. I don't know what kind of a person she really was. I suppose the only thing we had in common was that we were both in love with the same little girl.

Chemotherapy, of course, took its toll on the young patients. One of the less painful, but distressing, side effects of the chemotherapy and radiation procedures—especially to the little girls—was the loss of most or all of their hair. Some took this harder than others.

Sheila had long, shining black hair, almost to her waist.

When her turn came to say goodbye—at least temporarily—to her diligently cared-for tresses, Sheila didn't show much reaction—at least not on the surface.

Toward the end of the process, when there was little or nothing left, she pressed a small package into my hand. "Here," she said, "take this. Don't forget me."

On February 21, 1956, Sheila Marie Cameron, age 10, got her wings.

As for me, I gently wrapped the lock of black hair in its tissue paper, replaced it in the box with other of my treasures, and put it away in a safe place.

"I TOLD YOU SO . . ."

The small, 10-bed ward in The Hospital for Sick Children on Great Ormond Street in London had become as familiar to me as my own living room. Because of the painted frescoes on the walls representing the popular Punch and Judy puppets, it was officially called "Mr. Punch Ward." However, most of the child patients—and their parents—somewhat matter-of-factly referred to it as the "terminal ward," not because of insensitivity, but rather in an invariably less than successful attempt to acquire that often recommended but rarely achieved state of "acceptance."

None of the child patients—ranging in age from 2½ to 13 years and victims of leukemic-type diseases—could reasonably expect much of a future. Raymond, however, 3½ years old, with big blue eyes and curly blond hair, was the exception. The only reason Raymond was in the ward with the "terminal" children was that he was on a common regimen of chemotherapy with the other inhabitants.

Apart from the aforementioned eyes and hair, the aspect of Raymond's appearance that caught the attention of a visitor to the ward was his noticeably "knobbly" joints. A victim of severe childhood arthritis, Raymond had knees and elbows that were grotesquely swollen and misshapen. In fact, when he was admitted to the ward, he could barely walk and was in considerable pain. Chemotherapy, although not a panacea or a permanent solution, soon brought about what seemed an almost miraculous improvement in his condition, relieved his pain, and made him relatively mobile.

Raymond was a brave little boy. Although in a good deal of pain when he arrived, he rarely cried and never gave up his attempts to walk "like a big boy." After each of his frequent falls, he would grunt, pick himself up, and try it again.

Raymond's grandmother lived in London and visited him regularly. His parents, though, lived some 10,000 miles away, in the Falkland Islands, where his father ran a large sheep ranch.

More than anything—or anybody—else, Raymond missed his daddy. His daddy had promised to come and see him, and every day, as soon as he opened his eyes, Raymond would ask, "Is my daddy coming today? When will he be here?" The days, weeks, and months passed, however, and even Raymond's hope began to falter.

During my daily visits to my own little son, also a citizen of the terminal ward, I came to know Raymond pretty well.

As time passed, and the picture of his daddy in his mind began to fade, Raymond began to look to me for some desperately needed "daddying." Already a close friend of my almost-4-year-old Adrian—"Ady," for short—Raymond considered me the obvious candidate for a surrogate "daddyship."

When he saw me enter the ward, Raymond would stagger across to me as fast as he could and hold out his arms to be picked up. I would carry him across to Ady's bed, set him down, and do my best to divide my attention between the two boys.

The situation, of course, was not without obvious complications. When one day Raymond asked, in all innocence, "Ady, may I share your daddy?" a resolution clearly had to be attempted.

I fully understood Ady's objections: "You're my daddy. You're not Raymond's daddy."

I tried to counter the expected hostility with reminders that Raymond was only 3 years old, his daddy was 10,000 miles away, and he didn't get to see him every day. I tried to get Ady to see that Raymond needed our help.

The next day I was gratified to learn that Ady had been giving the matter some serious thought and had, he assured me, "talked to Jesus" about it.

From then on the mission in Ady's brief life became to support Raymond, who was, as Ady rightly observed, just a little boy and needed us.

"Raymond, listen. Your daddy will come. I know he will," Ady assured his despondent friend after yet another disappointing day.

"Your daddy comes to see you every day. Why doesn't my daddy come?" Raymond had never been so close to tears.

"Raymond, your daddy is miles away, across the seas, and he has all those sheep to look after." Young as he was, Ady realized immediately that this was not quite the reassurance his friend needed right then. He told me later that he asked Jesus what to say.

"Raymond, doesn't your daddy love you?" Ady continued.

Still a bit tearful, Raymond replied, "Yes, my daddy loves me."

"Didn't he say he's coming? Didn't he promise?"

A bit less tearfully, Raymond said, "Yes, yes he did."

"He'll come, Raymond. I know he will. He'll keep his promise. I know he will. That's what daddies do."

I wasn't fortunate enough, some weeks later, to be present on the wonderful day when Raymond's father did, in fact, arrive at the hospital after his 10,000-mile flight from the Falklands. I did, however, get a detailed report from the head nurse in charge of the ward.

"It was wonderful," she told me. "When Raymond's father walked into the ward, Raymond's little face lit up like a lantern. We didn't know the exact time of his daddy's arrival, so we'd said nothing to Raymond, and he was totally surprised. He gave an unbelieving squeal, ran across the room to his daddy, and scrambled up his leg like a kitten climbing a tree, until he reached his face. He almost yelled, 'Daddy, daddy, where were you?'

" 'Raymond, Raymond, I came just as soon as I could. I had some trouble with the sheep, or I would have been here sooner. I love you, Sonny.'

"And that wasn't all," she continued. "Ady was almost as excited as Raymond. He was having a transfusion and was confined to his bed because of his IV. But he bounced up and down in his bed in his happiness and excitement for his friend.

" 'I knew he was coming, Raymond,' he said. 'I told you. I told you so.' "

A few weeks later we were laying our small son to rest in the little Thames Valley graveyard. The sun was shining, the birds were singing, and the flowers were blooming, because once again it was spring in England.

Foolishly, perhaps, I spoke to my beloved little son before I left his graveside: "It won't be long, Ady," I assured him. "Jesus will be coming soon, and we'll be together again—forever."

I imagined I heard my little boy's voice: "I know, Daddy. I told you so."

TWO CANDLES FOR SAINT ANTHONY

His blue eyes, long curling lashes, and fair skin made him look almost like a choirboy. That, however, was just an initial impression. Eleven-year-old Jeremy may or may not have sung in the choir of the church he attended—if, indeed, he did attend a church—but he was certainly no angel. His innocent, ingenuous appearance left one unprepared for the tough little Cockney behind those clear, blue eyes.

Yet I quickly realized as I came to know him that there was a good deal more to Jeremy than met the eye. With increasing frequency, after a typically wary appraisal, he would perch himself on my little son's bed across from his own in the terminal ward of the children's hospital as Ady was dropping off to sleep early in the evening. Then, after my little boy was safely asleep, he would engage me in earnest conversation.

I suppose it could be called conversation. Actually, Jeremy talked, and I listened.

I came to think of him as a sort of attractively assembled three-layer cake: the angelic-appearing exterior disguising a tough, streetwise Cockney child—wise, in some ways, beyond his years—and deeper still, a kind and affectionate little boy.

We—at least, he—talked about many things, but most often about the other occupants of the ward. As long as they respected his "territorial rights," Jeremy got on well with the other child patients, whose ages ranged from around 4-years-old to the 12-year-old "senior citizens." Some, though, understandably, he liked better than others.

He especially liked Stephanie—but then it was impossible to not like Stephanie. Ten years old, she was—even with a shaven head and a painfully thin body, and disfigured by sundry tubes and other protuberances—an unusually pretty—no, beautiful—child. She too had cornflower-blue eyes, and it was still possible to see that her hair had been like golden silk. It used to hang down to her waist, her mother told us—Jeremy and me—a bit tearfully, and showed us a picture to prove it.

Stephanie was an unusual child. Perhaps because of her long—and losing—battle with a malignancy, she was at once quite childlike and yet old for her age. Her temperament, which matched her appearance, endeared her to everyone. Unfailingly polite, she never became impatient or querulous, even when her discomfort became acute. Always appreciative of any small service performed for her comfort, she smiled frequently, albeit sometimes through tears.

Jeremy quite quickly appointed himself guardian-cum-servant for Stephanie. Unlike the little girl, he was, for the most part, ambulatory, and he waited upon her untiringly, fetching and carrying, fixing her pillows, and generally doing whatever he could to lessen her inevitable discomfort.

Sometimes he would draw up a chair and just sit by her bed, not saying anything, holding her hand in his own, until she drifted off to sleep. No one said anything to him about his evident affection for the little girl. Even the youngest among us recognized that it wasn't the sort of situation to provide an opportunity for teasing. The other children realized, too, that if anyone had been inclined to make what they felt to be an uncalled-for comment, Jeremy was quite capable of taking immediate and violent action.

Perhaps as a result, to some extent, of our one-sided "conversations," Jeremy and I came to understand one another quite well over the period of some months when we saw each other almost daily. So when I chanced to look across at him one evening as I sat on Ady's bed watching him drop off to sleep, I was not really surprised to see the tears on Jeremy's face as he sat beside Stephanie's bed holding the little girl's hand as she hovered between waking and sleeping. He saw me looking at him but didn't turn away. He merely smiled faintly as he leaned over and wiped her damp forehead with a tissue he held in his hand.

I did not regard Jeremy as a religious child, his cherubic appearance notwithstanding, but I came to realize that the inside of a church was not totally unfamiliar to him. I knew he was—nominally, at least—a Catholic because of the rosary hanging over his bed, although I never saw him actually using it. I knew him to "go to church" only once during the period of our acquaintance.

One member of the staff of remarkably compassionate and dedicated nurses who cared for the "terminal" children made it a regular practice—on her days off—to stop by the ward and escort those of the children who were able to accompany her to a nearby park for an hour's play and change of scenery. Occasionally, if this activity coincided with my visit, I would go along and help push the children on the swings or join them in feeding the ducks on the park pond with bread brought from the ward kitchen for the purpose.

Jeremy wouldn't always go along with the expedition. Often he would stay behind to keep Stephanie company in the absence of the other children. If she was asleep or temporarily elsewhere for treatment, however, he would come along, and never failed to return with a bunch of flowers he had "appropriated" from one of the park flower beds.

One morning, however, after Stephanie had finally drifted off to sleep, exhausted after a particularly bad night of constantly recurring seizures and much pain, Jeremy accompanied the "park contingent" to the iron gates of the park and, as we were about to enter, beckoned to the nurse and whispered something in her ear. Upon receiving what was evidently her approval, he trotted off down the street and disappeared into the Catholic church about a block away. The nurse called me back from the group of excited children who were impatiently propelling me toward the duck pond, and asked me if I would mind dropping by the church to keep an eye on Jeremy and escort him back to the group in due course.

In a matter of minutes I found myself in the unaccustomed surroundings of the church. Though Protestant by heredity and persuasion, I have long been of the opinion that our common Father does not confine Himself to any one creed, place, or practice, but is available to us whenever and wherever we ask Him.

As my eyes accustomed themselves to the darkness of the church's interior, I saw that Jeremy and I appeared to be the sole occupants of the building. Jeremy was evidently unaware of my presence, and I drew back into the shadows, unwilling to intrude on his privacy.

Taking some coins from his pocket, the boy dropped them into the box provided, took a taper, and lit a candle, which he placed in a holder before a statue of a rubicund-appearing gentleman—evidently a representation of a saint. He genuflected perfunctorily toward the high altar, dropped onto his knees before the statue, and began to plead with the one represented. I remained standing silently in the shadows.

"Please, Saint Anthony," begged the boy, "ask Him to please help Stephanie. I know she's going to die, but please ask Him not to let her hurt so bad. Don't let her keep having those seizures. It hurts her so, and she's frightened. She's only 10, you know, Saint Anthony. She's just a kid. Please, dear Saint Anthony, tell Him if He has to have somebody hurting, let me hurt instead. I don't mind. Really I don't. I know I'm going to die soon, too. Tell him, please, Saint Anthony, to let me hurt instead of her. In the name of our Lord, Amen."

I saw the tears on his face as he passed by me on his way out of the church. He didn't see me, and I made no move. I waited for a few moments, dried my own tears, and followed him to the park gates, where he had rejoined the other children now congregating around the swings and seesaws. I nodded to the nurse that everything was under control, and we proceeded to take turns swinging the excited children until it was time for us to return the few blocks to the hospital.

Three days later when I made my daily visit to my little son, I noted that Stephanie's bed was occupied by a small boy. He looked to be about 7 years old. He told me his name was Ronnie.

I asked no questions, and nobody made any comment. It wasn't that sort of ward. Nobody—not even the youngest—ever asked why a bed was suddenly empty or occupied by a newcomer. Everybody—even the youngest—sensed it was something that nobody could bear to talk about.

Later I looked for one of the nurses I knew. "About three o'clock this morning," she told me.

"Was it bad?" I ventured.

"I've seen worse," the nurse responded, "but yes, it was pretty bad."

I looked for Jeremy, anxious as to how he was taking the tragic turn of events. He was lying—fully dressed—on his bed, curled up into a ball, with his back toward the other occupants of the ward. Clearly, right now Jeremy didn't feel like talking to anyone.

When I visited the ward over the following two days, Jeremy ignored me, as, indeed, he did everybody else. He spoke to no one, and if anybody approached him, he looked through them as if they were not there. On the third evening, however, somewhat to my surprise and, I think, to my relief, he joined me as I was about to leave the ward after watching Ady drop off to sleep. We walked into the corridor together.

He planted himself in front of me, his legs apart and his fists clenched. He looked straight at me. His eyes held fear—or hate—or despair? Possibly all three.

"I hate God," he told me quietly but vehemently. "He's a liar and a cheat. I don't believe there is a God."

Somewhat taken aback by the child's intensity, I was at a loss for a response.

I suppose I could have pointed out the obvious inconsistency of his statements. I could have spoken to him of the "reason" for human suffering and the necessity for faith and acceptance. I did none of these things. The little boy's outburst was too close to home. Realizing only too well where Jeremy was "coming from," I could not find it in my heart to rebuke him. I remained silent. I took a tentative step toward the white-faced child and took him in my arms. He was crying now. He stiffened at first, then relaxed and clung to me, sobbing.

After several minutes, he broke away and returned to the ward.

After this, Jeremy seemed to lose interest in everything. Time was running out for him. He had, it seemed, given up on life. Three weeks later, when I entered the ward and walked over to Ady's bed, I looked in vain for Jeremy.

Time was running out for my little boy, too. Several years younger than Jeremy, he firmly believed that he would be healed, that Jesus would make him "all better." I tried to believe too.

Not long after this, on one of our periodic "jaunts" to the local park, I left the group momentarily and, on an impulse, ran down the street to the nearby Catholic church.

Entering the dimly-lit church, I smelled the now somewhat familiar odor of incense and hot wax. Making my way over to the area where I had observed Jeremy on my previous visit, I, in turn, dropped some coins into the box, selected a candle—one of the fat, long-burning ones—knelt down in the place where Jeremy had knelt, and poured out my petition.

"Oh, God, can I change a prayer? I've been pleading with You for so long. Can I change my prayer? Oh, Father, please let him rest. Don't let him hurt anymore."

Not without misgivings, I rose from my knees and returned to the children and the nurse.

"Where d'ya go?" inquired 7-year-old Jamie as I rejoined the group.

"Mind yer own," admonished 9-year-old Annie, frowning at him. "'E 'ad to go to the gents, o' course."

Four days later, at two o'clock in the morning, my prayer was answered.

Now, years later, I never pass a Catholic church without thinking of Jeremy—the tough little Cockney with love in his heart.

Not infrequently, I reproach myself for not taking the opportunity to talk to him about the love of God, His compassion, and the need for acceptance of His will.

At the time, however, I had no words for Jeremy. All I could do was hold him. Maybe that was enough.

BRIDGE OVER TROUBLED WATER

It had been a long, long year—the last year of my son Adrian's brief life. The journey up by train to London's Waterloo Station had become almost routine. Then the 25-minute walk across Waterloo Bridge and on to The Hospital for Sick Children, Great Ormond Street. The walk to the hospital was not without enjoyment, for I was eager to see my son again and buoyed up by the somehow indestructible hope that today, by some miracle, he would be recovering.

But the return to the railway station in the evening was devastating. Once again, no miracle. Some evenings it became, as the French say, *insupportable.*

After putting my little son to bed in the ward, hearing his prayers and holding him in my arms while he fell asleep, I usually had plenty of time to make my way to the railway station. I frequently paused on the bridge spanning the River Thames to watch the broad river flowing along on its never-ending journey to the sea.

One evening I gazed, hypnotized almost, into the black, oily water and was not immediately aware that a woman had joined me. I looked up and saw her; she was standing quite close. I had seen her before in the shadows on the opposite side of the street and had recognized, without giving the matter much thought, that she was, almost certainly, of the sisterhood euphemistically referred to as "ladies of the evening."

"Evenin', Guv'nor," she said.

"Good evening," I replied, a little discomfited by her presence and unsure of her intentions.

She looked away from me and gazed into the Thames. "You been to the Children's," she said. It was a statement rather than a question.

"Yes, I have," I told her, a bit bewildered by her interest. "My little son is a patient there."

"Bad, ain't he?" she said.

"Yes, I'm afraid he is," I replied. And again, as much to myself as to her, "I'm very much afraid he is."

She reached out and touched my arm. I could see tears in her eyes. "I'm sorry, Guv," she said softly. Then she withdrew her hand quickly, turned, and walked away. I thought about the encounter all the way home and felt strangely heartened by it.

For the next few months I regularly made my way to and from the children's hospital, my emotions alternating wildly between unreasoning hope and complete despair. Often she would join me on the bridge.

"'Ow is 'e, then?" she would inquire. "Anything different? 'E's in Mr. Punch ward, ain't he?"

"Yes, he is," I agreed, wondering how she knew. "There's no change."

She never asked my name but invited me to call her Rosie. "That's what me friends call me."

"My son's name is Adrian, Rosie," I told her. "He's quite blond with gray eyes, and he's almost 4 years old."

She nodded and said nothing.

I came to rely on these encounters to a remarkable degree and one evening gave her a small picture of Adrian—a duplicate of one I carried in my billfold. I wrote on the back of it: "Thank you, Rosie." She looked at it for a long moment before wrapping it in her handkerchief and putting it carefully in her purse.

Then, finally, the telephone call came from the children's hospital: "I think you had better come at once."

He looked so small lying there, his gray eyes fixed earnestly on mine. I leaned over and wiped the perspiration from his forehead.

"Daddy, why are you crying? Daddy, I'm frightened. Oh, Daddy, is it going to be all right?"

"Yes, darling, Daddy's here. It's going to be all right."

The tiny hand clasped in mine relaxed its grip. When it was over, the two compassionate nurses put their arms around my shoulders and led me away.

I went out into the London streets—and it was night.

The following evening, after taking care of necessary business at the hospital, I stopped on the bridge and leaned over the railings, gazing, unseeing, into the water, trying to get a grip on myself. When I turned, Rosie was standing beside me. She touched me gently on the arm, just as she had the first time we met.

"'Ere," she said, proffering me something wrapped in white tissue paper. "They're for 'im. You'll put 'em on 'is grave for me, won't you?" Thrusting a tiny bouquet of lilies of the valley into my hand, she made a sort of choking sound, turned, and ran.

A mass of wreaths covered the grave. In the center of the profusion of floral tributes the tiny bunch of lilies of the valley contrasted sharply with the vivid roses, daffodils, tulips, and anemones that surrounded it.

I timed my return from my final visits to the hospital vicinity so that I would pass by Waterloo Bridge rather late in the evening. I wanted to tell Rosie that I had delivered her flowers. But I saw nothing of her. I could not imagine what had happened to her.

Summoning up my courage, I made my way to the nearest police station, not many blocks distant. With the unfailing courtesy and genuine helpfulness of the British police force, an officer listened to my story of looking for a friend. He eyed me a bit quizzically.

"Yes, sir, I am almost sure I know to whom you refer," he assured me. "She was regularly in the vicinity of the Waterloo Bridge. Her regular 'beat,' you might say. Her name was Rosie, wasn't it?"

"Yes, yes," I said. "That's the person I'm looking for."

"I'm sorry, sir," he told me quietly. "The person in question is dead. We picked her up in the street several nights ago. Apparently a heart attack."

"Did she have any relatives, any family?" I asked.

"No, sir, I'm sorry," the police officer said. "We went through her purse, but there was no identification of any kind. Cosmetics, matches, cigarettes, handkerchief, a couple of pictures. That was all."

"Do you still have her purse?" I asked. "Would it be possible for me to see it—to look into it?"

The officer hesitated. "Well, sir, that's rather an unusual request."

"Look, officer," I continued, taking out my billfold and withdrawing the picture of my son from it. "This is my son. If the person you picked up is really the one I am looking for, there will be an identical picture in her purse."

"Just a moment, sir," the officer said and retreated to an inner office. Within minutes he returned, carrying a brown purse with a large card attached, evidently a listing of the purse's contents. He looked a little excited.

"Yes, sir," he assured me, running his finger down the list on the card. "There are two snapshots in the purse."

He opened the purse and handed me two photographs. One was a replica of the picture I held in my hand. I turned it over and read in my own handwriting: "Thank you, Rosie." The other picture was of a small, dark-haired girl.

I had one more place to go. The following day I took the train to London and made my way to the children's hospital. I recalled Rosie mentioning that she had a friend, "Ben," who was a porter at the hospital. I inquired at the porters' lodge. A middle-aged man with a kindly face came forward.

"Yes, indeed," he assured me. "I knew Rosie. She used to stop by regularly, you know, and inquire about your boy. I used to get a report for her from the ward about him.

"She wasn't always in the line of business she was in when you met her, you know," Ben continued. "She used to be a waitress. It was after she lost her girl she went on the street. The little girl died in here, you know, 6 years old. It was about a year ago. That's when I first met Rosie—she used to come here and visit Gerda. That was the child's name. After the little one died, Rosie never went back to the waitress job."

"Ben, can you tell me where Rosie is buried?"

"No, Guv, I can't," Ben said. "But I can tell you where the child lies. Rosie used to go there every Sunday afternoon and cut the grass and take flowers. I went with her a time or two."

Soon I knelt beside the tiny mound. Lacking shears, I tried to pull the longest grass, growing lank and weedy now, with my hands. I filled the blue vase with water from the faucet in the corner of the cemetery and replaced it on the grave.

Unwrapping the tissue paper from the small bouquet I carried, I placed the lilies of the valley in the vase, thrust the paper in the pocket of my raincoat, rose from my knees, and walked rapidly away.

JUST ONE MORE TIME

A Requiem in Four Parts, Written in a Minor Key

Overture

It took some thought to decide where to take him. There were plenty of options, but as this would be the only opportunity—indeed, for some choices, at once the first and the last opportunity—he and I would have for his particular experience, it was not altogether easy to decide. So I made a short list—a very short list—because time was short.

First Movement: The Dance of the Flowers

Adrian—or, as he informed those who had not previously met him, "Ady, for 'specially"—stood with his arms outstretched in wonder and looked, just looked.

I had been there before, on a glorious spring day much like this one, but he had not. I hung back to give him space to try to absorb the incredible beauty he was seeing for the first—and the last—time. The acres of bluebells stretched in front of him, moving gently in the spring breeze, like a wonderful, gloriously beautiful azure carpet, except that this carpet was alive and moving.

I gave him a few moments, then slowly walked over to where he stood, arms still outstretched, gazing. Silently I put my arms around him.

"Oh, Daddy" was all he said. He had tears on his face.

Second Movement, Adagio: The Ocean

He had been here before—one time, when he was very young—and his ecstasies had involved paddling in the shallow water, investigating the tide pools for "creatures," and digging his bare toes into the damp sand. This time, however, I sensed it would be different.

It was, in some ways, a good deal like the encounter with the bluebells.

Here, though, the blue was not quite so intense, having a green shade to it, and the movement was more regular and, most strikingly, even more vast.

Again I watched from a safe distance as he waded out into the shallow water—the tide was on the ebb, appropriately enough—and stretched out his arms as if he were about to conduct an invisible orchestra, and just looked.

After a few minutes, when I couldn't stay away from him any longer, I approached him.

This time he turned toward me, the familiar tears trickling down his cheeks. "Oh, Daddy," he said, his eyes big and wide, "it doesn't have any end."

Third Movement: His Turn

Sometimes, though, it was Ady's turn to put into words what I knew and, I suspect, he sensed.

Most times he was asleep before I left the hospital to return to my home for the night. I had held him in my arms and kissed him good night before sleep overcame him. Occasionally, though, sleep would not come, and one night, having delayed my departure as long as I dared, I told him, "Ady, Daddy really has to go now to catch his train."

He held out his arms to me, tears welling up in his eyes. "Just one more time, Daddy," he pleaded. "Just hold me one more time."

Finale: Till We Meet Again

It is, I suppose, in this modern age, at least in Western cultures, the next-to-the-last stop in life's journey.

As I entered the funeral home, I felt, I think, a little like a condemned felon about to be led into the execution chamber. Someone gently ushered me, clutching my flowers in my hand, into an inner room. I was not seeing too clearly.

He looked so peaceful there in his little casket, his eyes closed, his long eyelashes casting shadows on his cheeks. Someone had folded his hands across his chest; I don't know who. It broke my heart that I had not been that person.

I approached the casket. No need to wait now—to give him time. I had no more time to give. "Ady, darling," I said, "I brought you some flowers. Rosie sent you some lilies. She never really met you, but I know she loves you. You would like her, Ady. She is one of God's beautiful people."

I leaned over to kiss him, and my tears fell on his cheek.

"Ady," I told him, "your angel is crying too. I can see his tears on your face."

I heard them outside the door. Because they were compassionate, a little shuffling of the feet, a clearing of the throat, to tell me they were there.

"Ady," I told him, "they are coming to take you away. I love you, my darling."

I turned to go, then moved back toward the tiny, vulnerable figure "holding" the lilies I had placed between his hands. I took him in my arms and kissed his hair and his face. Just one more time.

"Sleep well, my love. I'll see you in the morning."

SPIDER GIRL

When Adrian, my 3-year-old son, was diagnosed with acute lymphatic leukemia, a development totally "out of the blue," we were living in East Africa. I was the principal/teacher of the European Primary School for Missionaries' Children (a boarding school) near the city of Nairobi.

"Spider Girl," aka Veronica Anne, aka "Noni"—Adrian's not quite new sister—was 2 months old.

A tiny, green-eyed, blond-haired little person, she was, even at that tender age, clearly going to be tall. She had long, slender legs and arms.

We were counseled that it would be advisable that we take Adrian home to England for immediate treatment. We were not promised a cure; in those days, some 40 years ago, there was no cure available, only alleviation of some of the unavoidable distress and, perhaps, a brief postponement of the inevitable outcome.

An almost immediate departure was recommended.

It proved virtually impossible to book a flight to London for the four of us—myself, my wife, Ady, and Noni—at such short notice.

The Nairobi "European" community, however, was very close-knit, and "news," good or bad, traveled rapidly. The chair of what was then the British Overseas Airways Corporation, who had, in the company of several of his board members, just completed a tour of inspection in the area and was scheduled to return to London, hearing of our dilemma, kindly and graciously offered us his block of seats on a flight leaving the following day.

It was a 24-hour flight, with brief layovers in Khartoum and Rome. Ady, very excited by his first—and last—airplane ride (we had traveled from the United Kingdom to Africa by ship), greatly enjoyed the experience. Noni, unimpressed by the unaccustomed first-class accommodations that had been graciously assigned to us, slept most of the way in a "sky cot," a soft-sided mini-crib that, except for takeoff and landing periods, was suspended from the overhead luggage rack, swaying gently, and apparently soothingly, as we flew.

Arriving in London, Ady was immediately admitted to The Hospital for Sick Children on Great Ormond Street, a renowned children's hospital, where, during what was to be the final year of his brief life, he received the most compassionate and tender care one could possibly ask for.

In early April of the following year, not quite 12 months after our abrupt departure from East Africa, we laid our precious, little son to rest in a tiny cemetery near Newbold College.

Having spent much of my time over that long—or was it short?—year with my little boy, I had managed, with difficulty, to "keep it together."

Subsequently, however, with, it seemed, no longer a need to "put on a good front," I proceeded to "fall apart."

I saw no reason to continue to struggle. I no longer, I felt, had anything to live for.

It took me a little while—a very little while—however, to recognize how very mistaken I was. I began to get to know my little 14-month-old daughter, who had no intention of being ignored. Naturally, unaware of the situation, she, tiny though she was, was determined to have us—especially me—recognize that she was there and had every intention of staying around. She was not going anywhere.

In a very brief time, she single-handedly convinced me that I did, indeed, have something—somebody—to live for, and that she was that somebody. In a very short time, she managed to convince me of her sweet loveliness, of her need of me—indeed, of my need of her—and I fell in love with her.

We became inseparable. I took her everywhere with me—or maybe it was she who took me. She would wrap her long legs and arms around me and hang on (hence her sobriquet: "Spider Girl"). Where I went, she was going.

It took awhile, but slowly I began to heal—a little bit more and more each day.

Not that she filled the void. There is still a void. But she made her presence felt, not in place of the void, but beside it—a new and equally loved and precious person, who needed me, just as I needed her.

"Spider Girl" is now a beautiful, very tall young woman. She is a registered nurse and a teacher of "special" children. She is married to a Seventh-day Adventist pastor and is the devoted mother of four grown children.

She is still determined. She is still tall and beautiful. She is still—to me—"Spider Girl."

Infrequently, perhaps almost never, does the Comforter appear in our lives visually, or even audibly, in person, as it were. But, so very often, He comes to us, in an hour of need, in the person of a child of God, even in a tiny, very young child of God, to reflect, however dimly, the love and compassion of the Father of us all.

"I will not leave you comfortless: I will come to you" (John 14:18).

PAVANE FOR A PRINCESS

It was a perfect early summer day. The sky was blue, with a few fluffy, high clouds moving over the scintillating waters of the English Channel, blown by the cool, refreshing breeze. This same breeze stirred the long grasses of the sea meadows, and a slight movement was perceptible even among the stiff, wiry stems of the heather on the exposed cliff tops.

The battlements of the castle in the distance across the headland added enchantment to the scene, and my daughter and I, sighting the gray stones ahead of us, pressed on through the grass and wildflowers, pausing occasionally to sniff the salt-laden air.

Except for the presence of my young daughter, in her brief sundress and open-toed sandals, her long, auburn hair waving down her suntanned back, it looked just as it must have looked 300 years ago when another little girl, some six years older than my 7-year-old Victoria, looked across at the same meadows, the same cliffs, the same ocean.

Thirteen-year-old Elizabeth, however, was looking out toward the ocean from within the castle walls, the walls that constituted the limits of her world. Elizabeth was a prisoner, imprisoned for the "crime" of being the daughter of Charles Stuart (lately King Charles I of England, who had recently been beheaded by the Puritans, the infamous Roundhead riffraff that constituted the supporters of Oliver Cromwell, the self-styled "Lord Protector" of the Commonwealth of England, now a kingdom without a king).

Before his death, Elizabeth, a fragile child in indifferent health, hardly knew her father. Having spent most of her brief life in exile in France with her French mother and two younger brothers, she spoke English imperfectly and with an accent, and her memories of her royal father were hazy and colored by imagination. Yet for reasons not made clear to her, she and her brothers were to join their father in England.

The Lord Protector had seen fit, for reasons best known to his Puritan conscience, to concede to the condemned king's urgent request that he be permitted one last interview with his children before his impending execution.

It suddenly seemed desperately important to the lonely little princess that her father—almost unknown to her—would be happy to see her, would want her. No one else had seemed to care very much about her for what seemed a very long time. She barely remembered when she had not lived in France.

How is it possible to love someone so much and yet know so little of him? this impressionable, introspective young girl—more than a child, not yet a woman—must have thought. *I wonder if he will remember me. I wonder if he will like me. I know that I am not beautiful. I have heard the ladies of the court express their regret that I have not inherited my mother's beauty. I know I am not very wise. But perhaps, because I am his own little girl, he will like me just a little.*

Chroniclers of the time record that the meeting between Charles Stuart and his children, in particular the exchange between His Majesty and the young Princess Elizabeth, was emotional in the extreme. Even the Puritan guards, it is recorded, were moved to tears.

Having made clear to the barely comprehending children that this was the last time they would see him in this world—that before another sunset he was to be beheaded by his, and England's, enemies—Charles Stuart, on signal from his captors, prepared to bid farewell to the three he loved best.

He assured his daughter, the oldest and best able to comprehend the situation, that her father was no criminal.

"I am no traitor," he assured the weeping child. "I love England and have done no wrong.

"Darling, you will forget what I have said," he admonished the now almost hysterical girl, to which she vehemently replied, "I will never forget."

Torn from their father's arms, the three weeping children were ushered from the room by the waiting guards, but the princess, weeping hysterically, broke away from the soldiers and ran back into her father's arms for one last embrace.

True to her promise, the brokenhearted child, as soon as she had regained her composure, seated herself at the desk in her quarters and asked the lady-in-waiting to bring her diary.

"He told me he was glad I was come," she wrote in her childish hand. "He took me in his arms and kissed me. I do believe he truly loves me."

The following day was cold and blustery. "Bring me a warm doublet," Charles requested of his manservant. "I must not shiver on the scaffold. I would not wish my people to think that their king was afraid to die."

And later, when the executioner knelt and begged his pardon before striking the fatal blow, the king replied, "Gladly, my son. Do your work well. Strike hard and true."

Moments later, as the head of the murdered monarch was exhibited to the hushed crowd, it is recorded that a great moan arose, "as if the whole great city of London was mourning for their king."

The young Elizabeth did not long outlive her father. Confined by the Puritans in Carisbrooke Castle on the Isle of Wight, she succumbed at the age of 13 to what was described as "consumption." Members of her retinue are quoted by historians as reporting that the princess died of a broken heart.

Her diary is still in the room she occupied at Carisbrooke, locked under glass but visible to the visitor, a mute reminder of a young girl's love for the father she knew but briefly.

The princess herself sleeps in a grave on the grounds of Carisbrooke, overlooking the restless waters of the Channel and facing the coast of France, visible on a clear day, where she spent most of the years of her brief life.

My daughter Victoria looked for a long time at the yellowed pages of the other child's diary, suspended in time under the plateglass. "She was a sad little girl" is all she said.

On the way back we paused for a few moments at the resting place of the young princess. Victoria knelt in the lank grass surrounding the grave and read the inscription barely visible on the tombstone: "Elizabeth Stuart, Elizabeth I, Princess of England, aged 13 years." That was all.

She took the flowers we had brought and laid them gently on the small grave.

When she rose from her knees, she had tears in her eyes.

We walked away together. Neither of us looked back. Victoria grasped my hand tightly. "Oh, Daddy," she exclaimed, "I'm glad I'm not a princess."

"Sweetheart," I replied, "so am I."

"I'm glad, though," Victoria continued. "I'm glad her daddy really liked her. That must have made her happy."

"I know it did, darling," I assured her. "Every little girl needs someone who thinks she's perfect. Even a princess."

"DON'T LET GO OF MY HAND"

One of my favorite gospel recordings is one entitled "I'll Never Let Go of Your Hand." I never hear it sung without thinking of my friend Joanie, although the brief period when I knew her is now a number of years ago.

In my youth I had done some volunteer work with emotionally disturbed children, some autistic, others with varying problems, so I was not totally unprepared for her somewhat bizarre behavior when 7-year-old Joanie appeared in my Sabbath school room.

Joanie was a fragile-appearing little girl, small for her age, with big brown eyes in an appealing, heart-shaped face, her brown hair secured in two neat braids. I was not immediately aware of these last characteristics, however, because Joanie, having arrived in the Sabbath school room before me, was already seated at the end of a row next to two vacant seats, with her little green-checked dress over her head, effectively insulating her from the outside world.

The woman in charge of the room motioned to me to keep an eye on the situation, so I seated myself next to the new little one and waited for information and inspiration, silently beseeching the One who loves all the little ones for guidance.

Help was not long in coming. I felt a vigorous poke in my back and turned to face a small boy with whom I was already acquainted. Jeremy looked earnestly into my face and nodded his head in the direction of my small seatmate. "That's Joanie," he told me in a loud whisper. "She's dithsturbed."

"Thank you, Jeremy," I responded, genuinely grateful. This was a start. Now at least I knew her name. The other item of information I had already concluded on my own.

I turned toward her and took one of her hands in mine. "Hello, Joanie," I began, "I'm Mr. Milward; I work in this room. I'm glad you're with us in Sabbath school."

I neither anticipated nor received any response from the little green-checked "ghost" beside me, but she made no attempt to withdraw her hand from my grasp.

The Sabbath school program proceeded without untoward incident. Joanie resisted any attempt to reposition her dress, but she permitted herself to be "stood up" at appropriate times to "sing" and to be "knelt down" when it was time to pray. She made no sound the whole time and gave no indication of the least awareness of her surroundings.

The other children, many of whom were acquainted with Joanie and her unorthodox behavior from association in church school, paid no attention to her, evidently not regarding the situation as particularly abnormal.

When it came time for division into classes, the leader indicated to me that Joanie was to be in my class, and my half dozen children followed me to our assigned table. I led the way with Joanie, dress still covering her face, and we took our places at the table.

The class proceeded as usual, except for the fact that Joanie seated herself firmly on my lap, silently but vehemently declining the proffered chair, and clung tightly to my hand as I directed the lesson study and helped the children with the various activities planned for the day.

As I went around the circle asking questions and eliciting comments, the other children waited politely and patiently, without comment, as I gave Joanie her "turn" each time, although no sound or movement came from behind the flimsy cotton barrier she had erected between herself and the world.

The rest of the program passed without incident, and I decided that I needed a bit more information about Joanie if I was to help her at all. When her mother came for her, Joanie allowed her to pull her dress down to a more appropriate position and lead her out of the room.

I obtained Joanie's mother's phone number and talked with her the following day. I was told that Joanie, originally a bright, outgoing, but very sensitive little girl, had become progressively withdrawn over the past year and a half. I learned that she was receiving therapy and that the therapist felt, and her mother agreed, that Joanie's "problem," at least in part, stemmed from the breakup of her parents' marriage and the fact that she had been literally physically thrown out of the house by her father following a family disagreement. She was, her mother assured me, terrified of men.

Joanie had evidently decided, not unreasonably, that her world was not at all to her liking and she wanted no part of it.

I knew Joanie for about two years, and our friendship progressed from a muffled semi-communication to a warm and reciprocal affection.

The first "breakthrough," which came quite soon, was when she permitted her dress to be rearranged and made no attempt to put it back over her head. Then, a good deal later, she returned my smile with a smile of such sweetness that my heart turned over. "Thank You, Jesus," I whispered. "I knew there was a precious little girl in there somewhere."

After a while—a long while—Joanie "graduated" to sitting on a chair of her own in class, still, however, keeping a tight hold of my hand. I made one or two tentative attempts to disengage myself, all of which were firmly resisted. It was one of these experimental essays at disengagement that engendered the first words I heard Joanie speak.

I knew that she could hear well enough and was convinced that she was able to speak, but I was still taken by surprise when she leaned over to me, put her mouth close to my ear, and implored in a loud whisper, "Please don't let go of my hand."

By this time I was becoming quite skilled at one-handed teaching, so I made no further attempts at disengagement. It was Joanie herself who, some time later, voluntarily relinquished her grasp on my hand and began to engage, very skillfully, in the normal activities with the other children. Her classmates, immediately aware of the new development, made no comment, but exchanged secret smiles of approval.

The day the angels sang, however, was not long before Joanie and her family moved away from the community. In our Sabbath school any child who wanted to was invited to come to the front at "prayer time" to offer prayer.

The whole Sabbath school class was electrified when, following the invitation, Joanie seized my hand firmly and marched with me to the front of the room. We knelt down in the dead silence. No doubt patterning her technique on that of the local church elder, she fixed the whole "congregation" with a steady gaze from her big, brown eyes. "Let us pray," she invited.

Nobody laughed. Many of us were closer to tears than laughter.

Then Joanie prayed. She spoke clearly and distinctly in a sweet, well-modulated voice. She asked for nothing. Joanie's first public prayer was a "thank You, Jesus" prayer.

She thanked Jesus for the birds, the flowers, the trees, her mother, her little sister, her dog, her school, her classmates, her Sabbath school . . . then she thanked Jesus for her Sabbath school teacher.

I put my arm around her and hugged her, and my tears fell onto her hair and ran down the back of her neck. She didn't pull away.

It was a long prayer by primary Sabbath school standards, but nobody moved, nobody coughed, nobody fidgeted. When she was finished, we all said "amen" and got up off our knees.

One other thing we do in our Sabbath school is, when it comes time to pray, ask the children if they have any special requests or "thank You's" for Jesus. The following week, in response to the invitation, Danny, who was in Joanie's Sabbath school group, stood up. "I have a 'thank You, Jesus,'" he announced. "Last Sabbath, Joanie prayed."

The angels, I am sure, sang again.